Fabrics

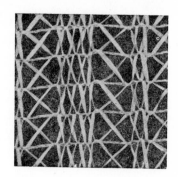

Fabrics

EIGHTH EDITION

Grace G. Denny

PROFESSOR EMERITUS

UNIVERSITY OF WASHINGTON

J. B. LIPPINCOTT COMPANY

PHILADELPHIA AND NEW YORK

Preface

NEW AND RADICAL CHANGES in the textile field have necessitated another edition of *Fabrics*.

This book was first published in 1923 as *Fabrics and How to Know Them*. The title was shortened to *Fabrics* in the fourth edition (1936).

Manufacturers of textiles have responded generously in authenticating trade-marked products. Firms dealing in laboratory equipment have furnished technical advice and courtesy photographs. The American Society for Testing Materials has permitted the use of photomicrographs, and Mr. Harvey H. Hannah of the Federal Trade Commission has approved the condensed statement of Textile Labeling Laws.

The author is especially indebted to Doris Brockway and Dorothy Jean Smith of the home economics faculty of the University of Washington for advice. Mrs. Helen Olsen of the training department of Frederick and Nelson, and Mr. Frank Vaculin, fabrics buyer, The Bon Marche, Seattle, have painstakingly criticized the textile definitions.

Seattle, Washington
March 19, 1962
GRACE G. DENNY

v

ACKNOWLEDGMENTS FOR ILLUSTRATIONS

FadeOmeter	Atlas Electric Devices Co.
Linen tester	Bausch & Lomb Optical Co.
Microscope Microscope	} American Optical Co., Instrument Division
Photomicrographs	American Society for Testing Materials
Scott tester	Scott Testers, Inc.
Spray test unit Spray test rating chart	} American Association of Textile Chemists and Colorists
Wool fiber photo-micrographs	The Wool Bureau, Inc.
39 Photographs	William Eng, University of Washington, Audio Visual Production Service
4 Line drawings	Mrs. Cecilia Carr

Contents

Fabrics

Fig. 1. Handwoven double cloth, black and white in fine cotton. Original by Virginia Harvey.

Part I   Fabric Definitions

Abaca (a-bah-kah). Plant native to the Philippines whose fiber is useful for cordage. It is often called Manila hemp.

Abrasion. Damage to surface of fabrics due to rubbing. Occurs, for example, on coat sleeves, upholstering, rugs.

Absorbency. Ability to take up liquids; important in dyeing. Wool has high absorbency.

Absorbent cotton. Raw fiber with natural wax removed. Comes in either fiber form, or gauze for medical uses.

Acele (a-seal)® acetate. Fiber for yarns in filament form.

Acetate. Generic term. See Legislation.

Acetate fabrics. Made from cellulose acetate yarns. May be woven or knitted, of fine or coarse yarn, used alone or in combination with other fibers or blended staple and solution-dyed.

Advantages: Resistant to moths and mildew, dyes readily with special dyes, dries quickly, holds permanent pleats and embossed patterns since moiré fabrics are durable through washing and cleaning.

Disadvantages: Weakened when wet, requires care in ironing, is harmed by nail polish remover, the blue color is sensitive to atmospheric fading unless treated for gas fading, and yarns will not take crepe twist.

Acid dye. Used for animal fibers, also Acrilan®, nylon, Orlon®.

Acrilan® (ac-ril-an). Acrylic staple fiber, usually crimped. Properties of acrilan fabrics: light weight, bulkiness, warmth; low moisture absorption; resistance to wrinkling, pilling, chemicals, moths, mildew and fungi; response to dyes; high tensile strength; resilience and capability of holding durable pleats. (a) Acrilan® alone or in blends with wool, cotton, nylon or

The symbol ® for registered trade marks is used throughout the book.

I

Orlon® is used for knitted or woven wearing apparel, blankets, carpets, work clothes.

(b) In fiber form, it is used for comforter filling, acrylic fiber-fill.

Other acrylic synthetic fibers: Creslan®, Orlon®.

Acrylic. Generic term. See Legislation.

Agave (a-gah-vay). Central American plant which yields structural fibers for cordage. Also called aloe. See Sisal.

Agilon®. Edge-crimped filament yarn, usually nylon, in fine denier, gives gentle stretch needed for women's hosiery. Manufactured in medium denier for textured yarns.

Airplane cloth. Plain-woven, mercerized cotton, with long staple ply yarns, 80 square or more. Uses: men's shirts, sportswear. See Balloon cloth.

Alaskine. French imported yarns, woven in U.S. Unique fabric of wiry, somewhat lustrous texture. Tightly twisted silk warp and two-ply silk and worsted filling. Women's outer apparel.

Albatross. Plain-woven, lightweight worsted used for negligées and infants' wear.

Alizarin dye. Synthetic dye closely related to natural alizarin from the madder plant.

Alpaca fabric. Plain weave, with cotton warp and alpaca filling; rayon may substitute in filling. Uses: linings, women's suits, men's wear. Term used interchangeably with brilliantine.

Alpaca hair. Fiber obtained from mountain animals native to Peru and Bolivia; related to the llama and vicuña, and having long, lustrous hair.

Aluminum foil. See Lurex®, Mylar®.

American cotton. Cotton grown in the United States; constitutes bulk of the world's production. Length: ⅝″ to 1¼″.

American-Egyptian cotton. Grown in California and Arizona. Has long staple, 1½ inches or more. See Pima cotton.

American Oriental rug. Term used in trade, but not approved by Federal Trade Commission. Pile rug woven on power loom imitating Persian rug designs, after the manner of Axminster loom.

Angora goat hair. Long, wavy, silky, fine, strong fibers. When manufactured, yarn is called mohair. Kid angora is finer, less durable. Yarns may be woven or knitted; or used in blends.

Angora rabbit hair. Fine, white, silky hair from a certain breed of rabbit. Warm and very light in weight. Blended with wool; used chiefly in knitted goods.

Aniline dye. Any dye derived chemically from aniline or other coal tar products.

Antron® nylon. Fiber with trilobal cross-section. It is light-weight and strong. The fabric is used to make sports jackets and other garments.

Applique. Fabric design, hand or machine sewn on a ground of net or cloth.

Argyle. Pattern of diamond shape in three or more colors, used for sports hose and sweaters. Originated in Scotland. May be hand or machine knit.

Armo®. Hair canvas interfacing. Yarn contains cotton, goat hair, rayon and wool. Comes in many weights. Resembles Hymo®, English term for hair canvas.

Armure. Silk, with a closely woven, pebbly pattern, chiefly used for neckties. Copied in any fiber or blend.

Arnel® triacetate. Continuous filament manufactured in both staple and tow types. Fabrics made from this fiber have the look and feel of wool but are resistant to moths and carpet beetles; also mildew and abrasion. Spun yarns are warm and bulky; adapted for knit outer wear.

Asbeston®. Heat resistant yarns, tapes, and fabrics made principally of mineral fiber asbestos with some cotton or synthetic fibers. Used for insulation jacketing, fire-fighting suits, electrical insulation, and ironing board and press covers.

Asbestos. Mineral fiber, mined chiefly in Canada. Straight lustrous fibers may be combined with cotton for spinning. Fire and acid resistant. See Asbeston®.

Astrakhan cloth. See Fur fabrics.

Austrian shade cloth. Cotton cloth woven with crinkled effect in wide stripes similar to seersucker. Used for window shades, especially in shops and hotels.

Avicron® viscose. Filament yarn, permanently crimped, having solution-dyed fibers; used for blending and tufting.

Avisco®. Name given by one company for its rayon and acetate products. Integrity tag gives data on fabric performance as to needed care: "washable," "machine washable," "dry cleanable." Avisco® acetate or Avisco® rayon. Licensed use of Avisco®.

Avlin®. Multicellular staple fiber. Can be bonded to other cellulosic fibers. Used also in nonwoven fabrics.

Avril® viscose. Rayon staple with new properties added. Can be mercerized. Residual shrinkage about 1 per cent after repeated washings.

Avron® viscose. High strength rayon staple fiber.

Awning fabric. Cotton, drill or duck in various weights. Yarn dyed for stripes; painted or vinyl-coated for awnings, garden and beach use.

Axminster. Pile carpet characterized by deep cut pile with heavy stuffer yarns which cause rug to bend crosswise but not lengthwise. Each tuft of pile yarn, row by row, is bound by filling yarn. Wide variety of colors and patterns possible.

Azlon. Generic term. See Legislation.

Back-filled. Starch applied to back of plain lightweight cottons to give them more body. Is not permanent.

Baize (bay-z).
  (a) Woolen fabric, slightly napped, imitates lightweight felt. Usually dyed green for billiard tables.
  (b) Cotton or wool baize for card table covers and lining display shelves.

Balance. Suitable relation of warp and filling yarns in fabric.

Balbriggan. Cotton, plain-knit fabric, lightweight; often finished with napped back for men's underwear.

Balloon cloth. Fine combed lightweight cotton fabric, having a plain weave and high thread count. Used for balloon gas

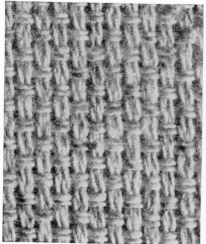 

Fig. 2. Basket weave. Monk's cloth 2 x 2. Fig. 3. Basket weave. Monk's cloth 4 x 4.

cells, typewriter ribbons, shirts, dresses; also made with rayon, nylon, or silk. See Airplane cloth.

BanCare®. Name for wide range of fabrics which have received nonresinous treatment for wet and dry wrinkle recovery. Licensed use of trade mark.

Ban-flame®. See Flame-retardant.

Ban-Lon®. Crimped type of continuous filament nylon or Dacron® which gives a textured effect when woven. End uses include bulk sweaters and lace and Ban-Lon® nylon for hosiery. See Textralized®. Licensed use of trade mark.

Barathea (Bara-thee-a). Name of a weave, usually twill, which was originally silk; but now largely replaced by rayon, cotton and blends. Used for neckties and women's wear.

Basket weave. Plain-woven fabric with two or more warp and filling yarns used as one, as in monk's cloth, Fig. 2, Fig. 3. In wool fabrics it is used for suits and coats. For modified basket weave 2-1, see Oxford.

Bast fibers. Inner bark of such plants as flax, jute, and ramie, when separated by retting process.

Bath mat or rug.
   (a) Small cotton or rayon rug, washable.
   (b) Chenille reversible.
   (c) Chenille nonreversible, with a canvas back often having
       a latex coating.
   (d) Woven rag rug.
   (e) Braided.

Bathrobing. Various fabrics such as terry cloth, in white or colors, and flannel or blended synthetics in napped fabric.

Batik (bah-teek or bat-tik). Javanese process of resist dyeing on cotton by pouring molten wax on the cloth according to a design, then dyeing the cloth, after which the wax is removed. Practiced by modern craftsmen on various fabrics; imitated in machine printing. See Printing.

Batiste. Soft, fine, sheer, plain-woven cotton of combed mercerized yarns; in white or pastel colors; printed or embroidered for blouses and infants' wear. Sheer wool is also often called batiste. Corset fabric called batiste is of the cotton broadcloth type.

Batting. Carded cotton, wool, staple rayon, or blends used for interlining and general stuffing purposes. See Sheet wadding.

Bayadere (by-ad-air). A woven, striped pattern with colors running crosswise; usually in silk or rayon cloth.

Beaver cloth. Thick woolen napped fabric originally made in England to resemble beaver fur. Used for coats. Also, a pile fabric with a cotton back which imitates beaver fur for hats.

Bedford cord. Worsted fabric corded in vertical ribs due to extra filling yarns on back. The cords are made round by stuffing yarns. Resembles cotton piqué, but cords are heavier. Cotton, rayon, worsted, or mixtures are used for uniforms, sportswear, and upholstery.

Bedspreads. Sometimes made to order from various fabrics but usually sold as finished spreads.

(a) Chenille, machine embroidered or loom woven to imitate hand-tufted or candlewick.

(b) See Ripplette®.

(c) Jacquard type cotton or combined with rayon.

(d) Marseilles type; usually white. Has raised Jacquard design with 2 sets of filling. Off the market.

Beetling. A flattening process on cotton, linen damask, or other fabrics. Surface of cloth is repeatedly pounded to add luster.

Beige (bayzh). Natural tan or ecru color; may be dyed.

Belfast®. Finish on cotton for self-ironing fabrics. Licensed process.

Bemberg® cuprammonium (coop-ra-monium) rayon.

(a) Filament, bright or dull, having a slight natural crimp. It is made in various deniers and is characterized by stretch spinning.

(b) Dress fabrics of filament yarns, usually sheers; either of the staple fiber yarns alone or in blends for suitings, knit underwear, linings. It is combined with acetate in cross dyeing.

Bengaline. Resembles poplin with heavier filling yarns. Made of silk, worsted, rayon, or nylon with filling of cotton or worsted. First made in Bengal, India. Plain weave is used for dresses, coats.

Bird's-eye weave. Small diamond shaped woven figure resembling a bird's eye.

(a) Cotton: filling loosely twisted for absorbency. Uses: diapers, towels. See cotton diaper cloth, Fig. 4.

(b) Linen is used for towels, runners.

Blankets. May be either plain or twill, of single or double construction, and are usually napped. They may be plain or patterned. The fiber content may be cotton, wool, rayon, Acrilan®, and other synthetics in various combinations and blends.

Moth proofing for wool: trade name Mitin®.

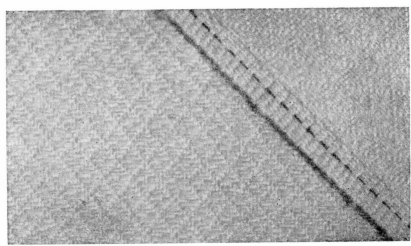

Fig. 4. Bird's-eye weave. Cotton diaper cloth.

Sizes:

Douple bed	80 x 90″
Twin bed	66 x 90″
Twin bed	72 x 90″
King size	90 x 108″

Bleaching. Process of destroying natural coloring matter in fibers; done in yarn or piece, usually by chemical process. Some linens are "grass bleached." White silk and wool, if bleached, tend to turn yellow upon repeated washings.

Bleeding. Tendency of unstable dye to run and stain other parts of the fabric. See Madras.

Blends. Two or more fibers combined before spinning. Fiber in predominance is always mentioned first. Viyella® flannel is a well-known blend of cotton and wool (to eliminate shrinkage). Examples of blends: Polyester with cotton, acrylic or wool; acrylic with rayon or wool. Rug yarns may blend wool with crimped nylon or rayon.

Block printing. Hand printing on fabrics with carved wooden or linoleum blocks as distinguished from power printing with metal rollers. See Hand print.

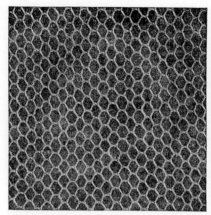 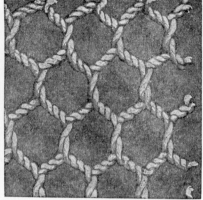

Fig. 5. Bobbinet.   Fig. 6. Detail showing construction.

Blotch print. Background color is printed leaving portion undyed for design.

Bobbinet. Cotton net, machine made, six-sided mesh which appears round. It may be nylon or silk. Made in fine grades for dresses and trimmings; coarse cotton mesh for curtains. Fig. 5, Fig. 6.

Boiled-off silk. Silk with sericin removed. Meaning is the same as degummed.

Bolivia. Woolen fabric, twill weave, with a soft, rich-looking nap; used for coats.

Boll (bole). Seed pod of cotton plant; contains cotton fibers or seed hairs in capsule form.

Bolt. Length of cloth from loom; rolled or folded. Called "piece" or "cut" of cloth. Bolts vary in length.

Bolting cloth. Stiff fabric of silk "in the gum," woven on hand looms in Switzerland. The plain or leno weave is used for fine sifting in flour mills and for screen printing. Nylon may substitute for silk. Metal screens are used instead for coarser grades of flour.

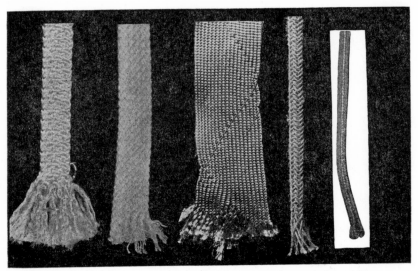

Fig. 7. Braids showing diagonal structure. Left to right: (1) rayon, tubular; (2) cotton shoelace, tubular; (3) rayon trimming braid, flat; (4) cotton shoelace, tubular; (5) silk soutache.

Bonded. Nonwoven. Various fibers in a web arranged in parallel or random form, bound together by *mechanical* means, with moisture and heat; or *chemical* means, with a bonding resin; or a combination of the two. See Nonwoven.

Bondex®. See Tapes.

Bonnaz (bone-az). A power machine which makes chain stitch embroidery for name labels on sheets, towels, etc. Used also for decoration.

Bontex®. See Shade cloth.

Boucle (boo-clay). Novelty ply yarn for knitting or weaving, using various combinations of fibers. Fig. 35. Some dress or coat fabrics woven or knitted use this yarn for a rough surface. Bouclé yarns are also used for hand knitting and hand weaving.

Braid. Differs from weaving or knitting. Several yarns cross diagonally as in straw hat braids, braided rugs, trimmings, shoe

Fig. 8. Brocade. Satin, pure silk. Note reverse side.

laces. Soutache and novelty braids are used for women's apparel. Fig. 7.

Brilliantine. Smooth, wiry fabric, with a plain or twill weave, cotton warp, and worsted filling. Or, it may have rayon filling. Used for linings. See Alpaca.

Broadcloth.

(a) A cotton material, plain, closely woven of single or two-ply yarn, and usually mercerized. Resembles fine poplin; does not have a square weave as does percale. May be plain or printed for apparel or household purposes.

(b) In silk, rayon or nylon, resembles texture of cotton broad-cloth.

(c) When manufactured of woolen or blends, in a twill weave, it has a lustrous nap. It is then used for dresses, suits, coats.

Broadloom. Refers to wide woven rug material, cut and finished any length. Widths: 9′, 12′, 15′ or 18′. May be velvet, Ax-minster, Wilton, or tufted.

Brocade.

(a) Jacquard weave in cotton, silk, wool or synthetic fiber combinations. The design is raised in contrast to the flat surface of damask. Originally it was made of heavy silk, in

Fig. 9. Brocatelle. Figure in rayon on cotton ground.

elaborate patterns, often employing silver and gold threads.
Background may be satin or plain weave. It is manufactured
in light weight for women's wear, heavy for draperies and
upholstery. Fig. 8.

(b) Obi brocades from Japan, of handwoven silk, are made
into suits and evening wraps. Modern copies are made of
rayon.

(c) Chinese silk brocade made in Hong Kong.

Brocatelle (broka-tel). Jacquard weave in heavy brocade with
a definite raised pattern on the right side. It is made of silk,
cotton, wool, rayon, nylon or combinations, also metallic yarns
for accent. Various textures and weights are made for evening
wraps, draperies and upholstery. Fig. 9.

Brushed knit fabric. Napped surface material, used for pajamas,
gowns and bed jackets. Made of cotton, wool, rayon, acetate,
nylon or combinations. It is flammable unless treated with
durable flame-retardant finish.

Brussels carpet. No longer made.

Buckram. Two-ply plain weave cotton fabric stiffened with glue
or other sizing. Used for hat frames, bookbinding and interlinings for purses and luggage.

Fig. 10. Burnt-out process. Wool pattern on nylon ground.

Bulk yarns.

  (a) Wool or Orlon® yarns which have the inherent property of giving bulk without weight.

  (b) Textured yarn; continuous filament, man-made fibers, crimped or by false twist and heat-set give bulky texture. See Stretch yarns.

Bunting (from German *bunt*—"bright," "gay"). Plain weave colored fabric, used for flags and decoration; a low grade dyed cheesecloth which tends to fade and bleed. May also mean cotton flags of heavier construction. More durable flags and signals use strong wiry worsted yarns.

Burlap or gunny.

  (a) Coarse jute, plain weave, natural brown or tan, used for gunny sacks and furniture wrapping.

  (b) Better grades, 50" in width, are bleached or dyed for drapery. Colors tend to fade.

Burnt-out.

  (a) Fabric in which lace patterns are produced by blends or combinations of unlike fiber groups, such as nylon and wool. The brocade effect appears after a chemical has destroyed the wool and left a design on the nylon ground. Fig. 10.

(b) Lace or eyelet effect where a chemical has burned out part of the ground.

Byrd cloth®. Mercerized cotton twill, fine yarn, high count, bleached, dyed vat colors; wind-proof and water repellent. Used in aviation garments, parkas, ski suits, raincoats, tents. Named for Admiral Byrd.

Cadon® nylon fibers. Multilobal, referring to the shape of a cross-section. Fabrics have a delicate texture; feel like silk.

Calendering. Finish placed on cotton or linen goods by heat and pressure to give a smooth surface; not permanent.

Calico. Plain weave printed cotton which originated in Calcutta. Calico is replaced by percale.

Cambric.
(a) White cotton fabric; plain, with a close weave, and firmer than nainsook.
(b) Linen. Fine, closely woven for collars, cuffs, church embroidery and handkerchiefs.
(c) Lining cambric (formerly called paper cambric). Stiff, glazed; comes in white and plain colors; will not launder. Used for pageant costumes.

Camel hair. Fabric usually woven in natural color of varying browns, sometimes dyed. Material is soft and lightweight. Fineness and luster vary with location on animal, also its age and condition; finer hairs are not sheared but drop from the animal. Typical coatings are twilled and napped. Camel hair yarn is also used in knit garments.

Candlewick. Bedspreads and curtains of unbleached muslin, decorated with tufts of heavy cotton yarn, cut or uncut. Originally a handicraft in the South, now imitated by machine and called chenille.

Canton crepe. Heavier than a crepe de Chine; originally silk, later mostly rayon. See Crepe.

Canton flannel. Heavy cotton fabric with a twill weave and with one side heavily napped. Used for sleeping garments, work gloves, interlinings.

Canvas or duck.
>(a) Firm, plain-woven cotton for sailcloth, awnings and other uses. Various finishes. See Awning fabric.
>
>(b) Embroidery canvas, called Penelope. A coarse, stiff cotton cloth, spaced for cross-stitches.
>
>(c) Coarse, open, plain cotton for hooked rugs.
>
>(d) Lining canvas of linen or cotton for tailoring.

Caprolan® nylon. Textured filament fibers for carpet yarns, crimped type.

Carbonizing. The removal by acid and heat of burrs and other vegetable matter in raw wool or woven cloth. In re-used wool, the similar removal of cotton or rayon.

Cardigan.
>(a) Three-button sweater type using heavy wool yarn in pronounced ribs.
>
>(b) Name of a rib knitting stitch.

Carding. Mechanical process of separating raw fibers of wool, cotton, or waste silk fiber, in preparation for spinning. See Combed yarn.

Carpet wool. Coarse, imported wool valued for its coarseness, strength and resilience.

Carpeting. Twenty-seven inches wide for stairs, sewn together for rugs; used chiefly in public buildings. See Broadloom.

Casement fabric. Made in variety of weaves and textures of mercerized cotton, rayon, mohair, silk, nylon, Orlon® or combinations. Used for draw curtains and screen fillers; usually neutral or pastel colors. Flameproof fabrics as Rovana® saran, Saranspun® saran.

Cashmere.
>(a) Imported hair of Kashmir goat, used for sweaters and coatings; blended with wool for reduced cost. Cashmere fabric is obsolete. See Kashmir.
>
>(b) Men's hose may be a blend of cashmere and nylon.

Cavalry twill. Worsted suiting with steep twill similar to elastique and tricotine. Uses: uniforms, riding habits, civilian slacks. Made in cotton or rayon for same purposes.

Celanese® acetate. Trade name for first acetate fiber made. Used for fabrics made of Celanese® yarns. Also Celanese® viscose, filament, staple, or tow.

Celanese® celaspun®. Spun acetate yarn.

Celaperm® acetate. Solution-dyed. Color is added to the spinning solution before the fiber is produced.

Cellophane. Generic term for viscose rayon in transparent sheet. Trade mark name in Canada. Cellophane tapes are manufactured in various widths: Texcel®, Scotch®. See Tapes.

Cellulose acetate. Chemical process for making acetate fibers and yarns. See Celanese®.

Cellulosic fibers. See Natural fibers. All man-made fibers whose origin is cellulose, such as rayon.

Challis (shall-ly) or challie. Originally silk and worsted made in Norwich, England.

    (a) Lightweight, fairly sheer, wool fabric; plain or printed for dresses, infants' wear, negligées.

    (b) Spun rayon similar to above. May combine with cotton yarns. Uses: dresses, sleeping garments.

    (c) Cotton, plain-woven, soft, lightweight, usually printed, for comforters, lingerie, draperies.

Chambray (sham-bray).

    (a) Plain weave cotton; typical: colored warp, white filling.

    (b) May have small woven figure or clipped spot. Uses: men's shirts, women's dresses.

    (c) Heavyweight cotton fabric for men's work shirts, described by weight.

Charmeen (shar-meen)®. Fine, smooth, worsted dress fabric with steep twill and high luster. Used for women's wear.

Cheesecloth. Plain, open weave cotton fabric yarns, unbleached, bleached, or dyed. See Bunting,

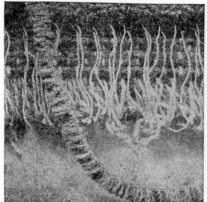

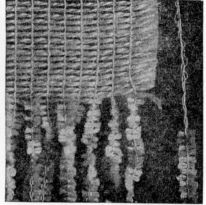

Fig. 11. Chenille rug.

Fig. 12. Process of making chenille yarn.

(a) Comes in many grades for a variety of uses: covering cured meats, wrapping cheese, making bandages, pads, curtains, decorations, and festival costumes. Thread count 20 x 12 to 44 x 40.

(b) Sold by the yard or in 5 or 10 yd. lengths or 30 yd. bolts for household uses. Comes in various widths, usually 36".

Chemstrand® nylon. Fibers made by one company.

Chenille (she-neel) rug. Fig. 11. May be either single faced Chenille rug or double faced heavy wool rug, manufactured from made-over carpets. See Bath mat, chenille.

Chenille yarn. Fig. 12. Yarn produced by weaving leno fabric; cut lengthwise between warps.

Cheviot (shev-e-ot). Made originally from the wool of Cheviot sheep. Resembles serge but is heavier and slightly napped for suits and coats. It is also made in blends of wool and other fibers.

Cheviot shirting. Coarse, plain weave cotton in checks or stripes. May be twill weave or small dobby pattern.

Chiffon (Fr., "rag"; pr. shee-fone or shif-on). Sheer silk, rayon, or nylon plain weave fabric used for dresses and scarves. Term

Fig. 13. Chintz.

also applies to velvet or taffeta made in a light weight with a soft finish.

China linen, or grass cloth. Not linen; an oriental fabric made from ramie fibers and used for tea cloths and napkins.

Chinchilla cloth. Heavy twilled woolen coating with a nubby surface. May be double faced with a plaid back. Lightweight chinchilla has a knitted back of cotton.

Chiné (she-nay). Warp print in plain weave silk or rayon, or in satin weave. After weaving, the design has a shadowy or blurred outline. Sometimes it is copied in direct print.

Chinese rug.
  (a) Pile rugs made by hand with tufts of yarn knotted on cotton warps; often carved after weaving to outline design.
  (b) Also hand hooked with coarse wool, usually in floral patterns. Back is of cotton or jute mesh; available in many sizes and grades.

Chintz. Originally, a printed calico from India, of plain weave, printed or plain cotton, glazed or unglazed. May be embossed or quilted. Uses: curtains, slip covers, dresses, aprons. Fig. 13.

Chlorinated wool. Fiber, yarn, or fabric treated with various chemical processes to resist shrinkage and felting.

Chromefast®. Solution-dyed acetate or rayon fibers.

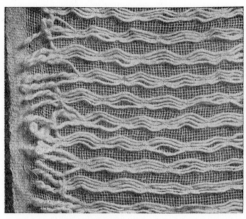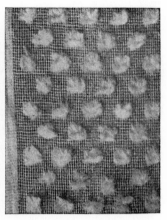

Fig. 14. Clipped dot. Float yarns of cotton roving (left). Clipped and brushed dots (right).

Chromspun® acetate. Filament, staple, or twist yarns, solution-dyed; resistant to sunlight, atmospheric fumes, perspiration, crocking, as well as to washing and commercial cleaning fluids.

Circular knitting. Fabric knitted in tubular form. Is produced faster than woven material; may consist of any textile yarn. See Jersey.

Ciré (Fr., "wax"; pr. see-ray). Finish given to fabrics or lace to produce a high luster.

Clipped dot. A woven dot at intervals using extra warp or filling. The filling is later clipped between the dots or figures. Fig. 14.

Coated fabrics. Large group of cotton fabrics treated in various ways to give an impervious surface. Oilcloth is the earliest example. Uses: window shades, rainwear, upholstery. See Plastic goods.

Coated yarns. Core yarns of cotton, rayon, or Fiberglas®; coated with vinyl film and woven for upholstery.

Coating. Woven or knitted fabrics for outer wear which come in various weights, compositions, and finishes.

Cochineal (koch-i-neel). Red dye derived from insects on cacti native to Central America.

Coco mat. Small rug used in front of an outside door, woven of coir, with a deep brown pile or brushlike surface.

Cocoon. Protective covering of silkworm which becomes a chrysalis surrounded by a long filament of silk and silk gum.

Coir (kwor). Coarse brown fiber from the shell of a cocoanut; used in coco mats.

Coloray® viscose. Either a solution-dyed rayon staple fiber, or one of cotton, wool, flax, or silk. The fabric is fast to light, withstands severe washing and perspiration, and resists crocking.

Colorspun®. Solution-dyed rayon or acetate fiber.

Combat cloth®. Nylon fabric of high thread count, made with a special weave for exceptional strength and slippage resistance; lighter in weight than Tackle twill®. It is used for football uniforms.

Combed yarn. Cotton or wool having long staple, parallel fibers; superior to carded yarn in luster and strength.

Combination yarns. Not to be confused with blends. Ply yarns combine yarns of different composition or textures, such as metallic or elastic yarns. See Novelty yarns.

Combination fabrics. Composed of warp and filling yarns each of a different fiber.

Compound fabric. Woven of two or more sets of warp or filling or both. Double, triple, and other multiple cloths are made this way, as are heavy figured fabrics and some webbings.

Conditioning. Determination of moisture content in textile materials. True weight is estimated according to specific temperature and relative humidity.

Connemara. Irish homespun, heavy, with a loose weave, made in black and white. It resembles Donegal. See Tweed.

Continuous filament. Natural form of reeled silk or man-made fibers in filament form.

Fig. 15. Corduroy of different wales and weights.

Contro®. Name of rubber yarn made by one company.

Converting. All processes applied to gray goods after they have left the loom; term includes bleaching, dyeing, printing, and finishing.

Cord.

(a) Two or more ply yarns twisted together to form cord.

(b) Surface rib effect in fabrics.

Cordino®. Combed cotton, fine wale, resembles Bedford cord but has a different weave. Is made with wash and wear finish and is machine washable.

Cordura® viscose. Rayon filament with high tenacity, used for tire and apparel fabric.

Corduroy. Cotton fabric with lengthwise wales of cut pile. Fig. 15. Is usually Sanforized and mercerized; may have a rayon pile.

(a) Pin wale corduroy is lightweight for children's and women's wear.

(b) Heavy firm "cords" are made for work clothes and sportswear.

(c) Drapery and upholstery fabric is woven wide.

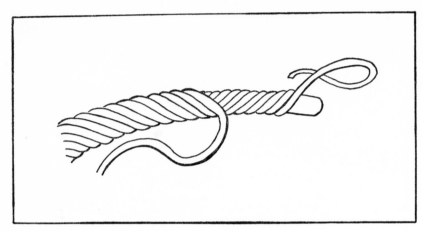

Fig. 16. Core yarn. See Lastex®.

Core yarn. Yarn with core or center of a different yarn, such as
  rubber. Lastex®.
  Yarns for wrapping core may be of any suitable fiber, and there
  may be two wrappings, as in Fig. 16.

Corset or brassière (bra-zeer) fabrics. Cotton, rayon, nylon,
  silk, and/or rubber in batiste, brocade, coutil, net, or mesh.
  Not sold by the yard.

Corval®. Cross-linked cellulosic fiber, having a soft, bulky, wool-
  like hand. It blends with wool and acrylics such as Orlon®,
  absorbs dyes readily, and resists pilling. See Topel®.

Cotron®. Fabrics made of cotton and Avisco® rayon. They are
  soft and durable; may be plain or printed. Uses: apparel,
  especially men's shirts and shorts.

Cotton fiber. Differs in length, diameter, strength, and twist
  according to the variety and geographical distribution of the
  parent plant. Cotton as well as linen yarns have added
  strength when wet.

Cotton satin. Characterized by warp face weave, superior to
  sateen; may be solid color or print. Highly mercerized to give
  added permanent luster. See Polished cotton.

Cotton waste. Lint and yarn refuse in mills, used for cleaning purposes. Broken ends of yarn used in paper manufacture.

Cotton yarn number. Indicated in terms of units of length per unit of weight.

No. 1 cotton — 840 yards per pound.

No. 10 cotton — 8,400 yards per pound.

No. 100 cotton — 84,000 yards per pound.

Cottonade. Heavy cotton twill, usually having blue and white stripes, used for men's work clothes. Resembles hickory shirting.

Count.

(a) Number of warp and filling yarns per inch in woven cloth; called thread count. Warp indicated by first number. For example, a count of 68 x 52 means 68 ends in warp and 52 picks in filling.

(b) Also size or weight of yarn. See Cotton yarn number. See Tests—thread count.

Course. In knit goods a row of loops across the fabric.

Coutil (koo-teel). Firm cotton, twill fabric, herringbone or figure weave for corsets and brassières; also of rayon, nylon or combinations.

Covert (kuv-vert). Cotton or worsted fabric of twill weave. Warp is composed of 3-ply yarns, one of which is white.

Crash. Plain weave cotton, linen, spun rayon, or blends; usually of uneven yarns. Used for toweling, table linen, dress fabrics, draperies; comes in various weights, textures, colors.

Cravenette®. Process of making fabrics and garments water repellent. Finish is renewable.

Crease resistant. Durable finishes on cotton, rayon and linen fabrics, for wrinkle resistance and recovery. Sold under various trade names.

Crepe.

(a) Plain weave with filling yarns of high twist which produce kinky surface. Manufactured of cotton, silk, rayon, and nylon for women's apparel.

(b) Wool crepe. Lightweight dress fabric with characteristic crepiness.

Crepe back satin. Silk fabric with lustrous satin warp. Crepe twist yarns are used for filling. This fabric is reversible.

Crepe de Chine. Silk fabric, plain weave, with crepe twist filling yarns and alternating S and Z twist in groups of two. Used for dresses, lingerie, linings.

Crepe yarn. High twist yarn in single or ply. Tends to contract during finishing. Silk and rayon are most extensively used in crepe fabrics.

Creslan® acrylic. Staple fiber with affinity for dyes; blends with wool. Fabrics have pleat retention, crease and wrinkle resistance, quick drying properties. Used for dress fabrics, upholstery and carpets.

Cretonne. Plain weave, printed drapery and upholstery fabric of cotton, linen, rayon, or mixtures. Term seldom used.

Crinoline. Stiff, open, plain weave cotton highly sized with dull finish. Used for interlinings or skirt lining to give stiffness.

Crocking. Surface dye which rubs off cloth.

Crofting. Grass bleaching; term used in Scotland and Ireland.

Cross-dyeing. Process required when fabrics contain fibers of different dye affinity, such as cotton and wool or rayon and acetate.

Cross-linked. Modified rayon with improved properties of wet strength and dimensionable stability. See Corval®, Topel®.

Cupioni® (koop-e-oni). Cuprammonium filament rayon yarns, having thick and thin irregularly spaced slubs. Fabric resembles silk doupione. Used in combination with cotton and other rayons (filament and spun) and with silk. End uses include blouses, dresses, and shirts. Blends with rayon and silk are used for curtains and bedspreads.

Cuprammonium (koop-ra-monium) rayon. Yarn or staple made by cuprammonium process. Often identified with Bemberg®.

Curad®. See Tapes.

Fig. 17. Damask. Double damask, linen.

Curon® (cure-on). Multicellular foam laminated to woven or knitted fabric. Varies in thickness from ¹⁄₁₆″ to 5½″ for end uses. Also bonded to washable glove fabric, shoe soles. See Insulating materials.

Cyana® (sy-ana). Name for several quality controlled chemical finishes, such as Permel Plus®, which are usually applied to cottons. They are water repellent, spot, stain, and wrinkle resistant.

Dacron® (day-kron) **polyester.** Fibers are produced both in filament and staple form. The fabric is strong and resilient; resistant to abrasion, moths, mildew; retains pleats because it is thermoplastic; resists stretching; and is quick drying.

Uses: shirts, women's apparel, drapery, upholstery, sails. May be used alone or in blends with wool or cotton.

The typical blend for shirts: Dacron® 65%, cotton 35%; requires little ironing. Commercial bleach may be used on white Dacron®.

Dacron® fiber-fill. Staple form of Dacron®, comes in bats to be used in comforters, pillows, sleeping bags, apparel.

Damask. Origin: the ancient city of Damascus. Characterized by a flat and reversible Jacquard weave.

(a) Table damask is made of linen, cotton, rayon and cotton, or other combinations. Material may be sold as yardage in varying widths or as patterned cloths with napkins.

(b) Linen may be single or double damask, having 5 or 7 float yarns, the latter being more closely woven. Weave shows the design by contrast of warp and filling face. Fig. 17.

(c) Cotton damask, mercerized and always single damask, is much used in commercial dining rooms. It may be white resembling linen damask or woven in small checks alternating white with red, blue, green or yellow.

(d) Upholstery damask, in any combination of fibers, may be used in making draperies.

Darvan®️ nytril. See Legislation.

Decating. Process of sponging certain types of wool fabrics to stabilize their dimensions and to improve the luster.

Degumming. Process of removing sericin from silk yarns or fabrics.

Delustering agent. Colorless pigment used to dull the luster on some man-made filament fibers. Used in making designs. See Pigment print.

Denier (den-yer). Unit of yarn number. It was originally a French unit of weight for silk yarns. Designates fineness of yarns of silk, rayon, nylon, or other man-made fibers, commonly applied to women's hose. The smaller the denier number, the finer the yarn. (15 den. is twice as fine as 30 den.).

Denim. (Fr., *serges de Nimes,* from twilled fabric originally made in Nimes.) Heavy cotton twill, usually having an indigo dyed warp with white filling yarns. Used for work clothes. May be plain, striped or plaid. Made in lighter weight for sportswear and slip covers.

Diaper cloth.

(a) An absorbent cotton fabric; may be bird's-eye weave, knit goods, or cheesecloth. Used for infants' diapers.

(b) Diaper weave. Diamond or lozenge pattern of silk in ancient times.

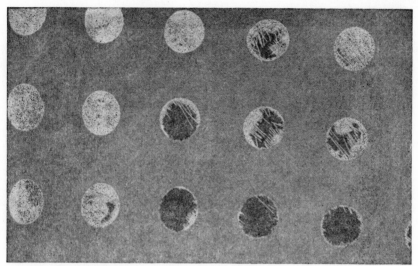

Fig. 18. Discharge print. Fabric shows damage by chemical action.

Dieldrin (deel-drin). Common name for widely used insecticide. Mill treatment for mothproofing wool. Rigid licensing specifications govern the use of this process.

Dimity. Sheer cotton fabric of carded or combed yarns. It has a plain weave with lengthwise cords or squares made by grouped yarns and may be white, dyed or printed. Used for blouses, lingerie or dresses.

Discharge or extract print. Used on dark color goods to produce a white or light design. Fig. 18. The color in dyed cloth is bleached or discharged in spots, leaving a white design. May be printed with medium resistant to dark dye.

Disciplined®. Cotton fabrics treated with a patented process which gives them durable wash and wear properties, and makes them quick drying, and wrinkle, soil, and shrink resistant.

Disposable clothing. Paper products being developed for garments to be thrown away after one wearing. See Nonwoven.

District checks. Scottish patterns in suitings and tweeds. Example: shepherd's check. See Tweed, Glenurquhart.

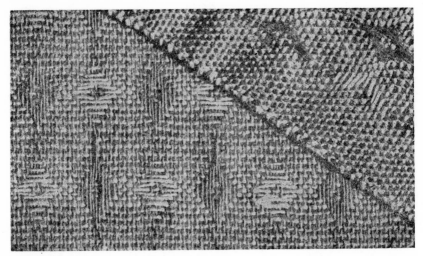

Fig. 19. Dobby weave. Cotton.

Dobby weave. Loom used for producing small woven patterns such as huck and honeycomb. Any small figure not requiring a Jacquard loom. Fig. 19.

Doeskin. Heavy, short-napped woolen fabric used for men's coats. Also heavy twilled cotton, napped; used for sports coats.

Domestics. Term used for such household textiles as sheets and towels.

Domett (dom-et). Same as outing flannel. Old term, little used.

Donegal. Thick, rough, hand-woven tweed named for county Donegal, Ireland. Characterized by spots or slubs of white or colors in the yarn. Imitated in machine-woven Donegal type tweed. Fig. 63.

Dotted Swiss. Machine embroidered or woven dots on sheer cotton ground. See Clipped dot, Fig. 14.
See Flock, Fig. 23.

Double cloth.
(a) Figure-woven, reversible, and having 2 sets of warp yarns and 2 of filling. Fig. 20. See Fig. 1.

Fig. 20. Double cloth. Red and white cotton tablecloth hand woven in India.

(b) Coatings are of a plain color on one side, with plaid on the reverse. A fifth yarn is used to bind the 2 layers together.

(c) Double construction blankets have 1 warp and 2 fillings.

(d) Double cloth may combine two different weaves, such as twill, satin, pile, or Jacquard. An example is satin-faced velvet ribbon.

Doupione or doupion (doop-e-own). Word is of Italian origin, meaning an irregular silk yarn spun from double cocoons. It makes rough-textured silk dress and drapery fabrics. See Cupioni®.

Dressing. Sizing made of gum, glue, or starch, which is used for finishing various fabrics.

Dri-don®. Finish for shrinkage control.

Drill. Similar to denim, having a 2/1 twill weave. Usually dyed khaki for uniforms. In a lighter weight it is called "jean," and used to make play clothes. Pocket drill is used for linings and pockets.

Drip dry or wash and wear. Cotton fabrics which may be washed and worn without ironing because of their shrink and wrinkle-resistant finishes. Drip dry garments must hang dry and must not be tumbled in a machine. Used for pajamas, shorts, dresses, children's wear.

Drugget. A heavy, coarse, reversible rug with no pile. It is woven in India with cotton warp and filling of jute and camel's hair.

Duchesse satin. Heavy, rich-looking satin of silk or rayon.

Duck or canvas.

(a) A heavy cotton plain weave fabric having ply yarns, or single warp yarns in pairs. It may be bleached, or unbleached; piece-dyed or yarn-dyed; painted or printed, for a variety of uses.

(b) Army duck is sold by weight. Tents, army cots, tarpaulins, government mail bags, filter cloths, laundry-machine aprons are all made of wide-width duck.

Dungaree. Coarse cotton fabric of characteristic blue, used for sailors' work clothes; a type of denim.

Duplex print. Pattern printed on both face and back of fabric. May be identical or of different colors.

duPont® nylon. duPont® rayon. Fibers made by one company.

Durene®. Combed, mercerized, cotton 2-ply yarn used in knitted and woven goods.

Duvetyn (dove-teen). Originally French fabric made of soft woolen yarns with a close-cut nap of rayon, silk, or cotton. See Suede cloth.

Dyeing. Process of coloring textiles. Acetate and other man-made fibers require a special type of dye.
Animal fibers, wool and silk, have a natural affinity for dyes.
Cross-dyeing. See Cross-dyeing.
Ingrain. Yarns dyed before knitting or weaving.
Piece-dyeing or dip-dyeing is done after weaving or knitting.
Stock-dyeing. Fibers dyed before spinning as "dyed in the wool."

Yarn-dyeing. Yarns dyed before weaving or knitting as for plaids or stripes.

Solution-dyeing. Pigment incorporated in the solution for man-made fibers before spinning.

Dyes. Classified as to source.

Natural. Used originally by primitive peoples and pioneers; now only by some craftsmen.

Animal: cochineal.

Mineral: copperas.

Vegetable: logwood, and other sources.

Synthetic. Used commercially. Derived from a coal tar base by a process discovered by Sir William Henry Perkin in 1856 in England.

May be acid, basic, direct, mordant, sulphur, vat, etc.

Dylanize®. Process for wool shrinkage control in wool or wool blends of knitted or woven goods. Term used only by licensees. Dylan®. Term used in Canada, England and Scotland.

Dynel® (dye-nell) modacrylic. Fiber in staple form, yarns made of which are valuable for their bulking quality. Fabrics dry rapidly and can be heat set. They are also valued for the softness, bulk, warmth, and strength which are desirable for blankets, and coating, especially pile fabrics. Many blends are used for knit underwear. One hundred per cent Dynel® is used for filters, industrial items.

Ecru (ay-kroo). Light tan color, deeper than cream.

Egyptian cotton. A long-staple, (up to 1⅜″) fine, strong, fiber grown in Egypt, and having a brownish color. Used in knit goods, also for the warp in hand weaving. See Pima cotton.

Eiderdown. Name for a woven wool fabric with napped surfaces on both sides or a single-faced fabric with a cotton knit back and a wool nap. Used for infants' and children's wear.

Eighty-square fabric. Good grade of cotton fabric; usually refers to 80-square percale. See Square weave.

Elastic yarns. Made from a core of cut rubber wound with cotton, rayon or nylon yarn for woven or knitted elastic fabrics. Known by trade names Contro® and Lastex®.
See Lycra®, Stretch yarns, Spandex.

Elastique. Firm worsted suiting with steep double twill, similar to tricotine. Used for army uniforms, riding breeches, civilian slacks. When made of rayon or cotton, it is used for the same purposes.

Electric blanket. Two pieces of blanket fabric, of any fiber, mixture or blend, that enclose an electric heating element made of especially insulated flexible wires. The blanket is made waterproof, flame resistant, durable, and washable. A label gives directions for care.
Safety guaranteed by underwriters.
Must never be dry cleaned.
They come in the following sizes:
  66 x 84
  72 x 84   King size 86 or 95 x 103.

Embossing. The process of pressing a temporary design into a fabric with hot engraved rollers. Permanent patterns are produced on acetate. See Moiré.

Emerizing. A fine nap is raised on cotton glove fabric with emery cloth to make it resemble suede leather.

End. Warp yarns are referred to as ends; wefts, as picks.

End-to-end cloth. Plain-woven gingham type fabric; usually used for men's shirts or children's wear. Characterized by alternating colored and white warp yarns.

End use. The ultimate purpose; for example, a knit sweater; for which a certain yarn was produced.

Enka® nylon. Fibers made by one company.

Enka® rayon. Brand of rayon manufactured by viscose process. Fabrics made of Enka® yarns, so labeled.

Éponge (Fr., "sponge"; pr. ay-pongzh). Soft, loose, plain-woven fabric of novelty yarn similar to ratiné. May be cotton, wool, silk, nylon, or rayon. Used for dresses, suits. Term is little used.

Epoxy. Resin finish for mill use on wool to minimize shrinkage. One of many new types of resin finishes.

Estron® acetate. May be either filament yarn or tow; the product of one company.

Etamine. Plain weave, lightweight, open fabric of cotton or wool, heavier than voile. Made also with other fiber yarns.

Everfast®. Family of cotton and rayon fabrics with an unqualified color guarantee.

Everglaze®. Finish on cotton and rayon fabrics which gives wash and wear; wrinkle and spot resistance. Used with Ban-Care®. Licensed use of trade mark.

Evershrunk®. Preshrunk finish whose residual shrinkage is not in excess of 2 per cent.

Express stripe. Heavy twill blue and white striped denim, used for work uniforms. See Hickory stripe.

Fabric. Cloth, woven or knitted of yarns of any textile fiber. Nonwoven goods may replace woven fabrics.

Fabric gloves. Warp knit fabric, smooth or napped, of cotton, rayon or nylon.

Fabrikoid®. Coated fabric on cotton base; pyroxylin treated; and made in various weights, colors and embossed patterns. Used for bookbinding, upholstery, furniture, and auto seats.

Fabrilite®. Vinyl coated fabric, made in smooth or varied textures, for upholstery, auto seat covers, bookbindings, folding doors and luggage. Water resistant, soap and water washable.

Faconné (Fr., pr. fah-son-nay). Surface pattern made by small woven self-color figures.

Fading. Loss of color from dyed yarns of fabrics due to strong sun or other light, washing, or bleaching.

Faille (file). Soft ribbed silk, rayon, Arnel® acetate, or cotton fabric, lighter and smoother than grosgrain.

Felt.

    (a) Material, usually of wool or hair matted by use of heat, moisture, and pressing. May also be first woven, and then shrunk to a felt. Texture varies with uses: pennants, table covers, hats, slippers.

    (b) Blends of different fibers may be bonded for felt. See Bonded fabric.

    (c) Pellon®, a form of nonwoven felt.

    (d) Decorative felts. See Feutron® for draperies, wall covering, and upholstery.

Feutron® (few-tron). A felt for draperies and other decorative uses of 65 per cent Dacron® and 35 per cent viscose. It is hand washable, light-fast, and is used for die-cut patterns.

Fiber. Smallest unit of textile material. May come from a natural source such as cotton, wool, flax, or silk; or be a man-made filament.

Fiberglas®.

    (a) Fine filaments drawn from refined molten glass assembled to make yarns of great strength. They are soft, pliable, and resistant to soil, chemicals and heat.

    (b) Fabrics made from glass yarn for marquisette and printed hangings; fireproof and unaffected by sunlight.

    (c) Industrial uses: In fiber form for heat insulation; in tape form for electric insulation; in molded form for boats, awnings.

    (d) Woven: Screen mesh to replace wire screening. See Fiber glass PPG.

Fiber glass PPG. Drapery fabrics using patterns designed by leading decorators. See Fiberglas®.

Fibers. See Cellulosic, Man-made, Mineral, Natural, Protein, Synthetic, Vegetable.

Fiberset®. Stabilizing finish on silk, rayon, and some mixtures.

Fibroin. Silk filament as secreted by the silkworm without any coating of gum or sericin.

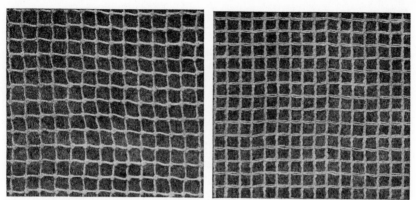

Fig. 21. Filet net, hand-knotted.   Fig. 22. Machine reproduction.

Filament. Single element of silk; or any man-made fiber as it comes from the mechanical spinneret.

Filature. Factory for reeling raw silk.

Filet (fee-lay). Mesh knotted by hand as in fish nets, hand-made lace, and hair nets. Fig. 21. Machine imitated. Fig. 22. See Net.

Filling.

(a) Crosswise yarn in weaving (pick).

(b) Also finish as starch or china clay on cotton. See Weighted silk.

Finishes. Treatment of fabrics to prepare them for specific end uses. See Finishing.

Specific finishes:

(a) For crease resistance, some examples: Belfast®, Everglaze®, Bancare®, Stazenu®, Disciplined®.

(b) For flame retardance: Banflame®, Pyroset®.

(c) Glaze, durable: Everglaze®.

(d) For moth repellency: Mitin®.

(e) For odor and germ resistance: Kenisan®, Sanitized®.

Finishing. Preparation of gray goods for market. Refers to all processes after weaving: bleaching, dyeing, napping, printing, sizing.

Fireproof. Asbestos or Fiberglas® make fireproof fabrics. They will not burn.

Flame-proofing treatment of fabrics.

(a) Used on cellulosic fibers only; sold under various trade names, such as Ban-flame®. Licensed users issue certificates; recognized in fire insurance claims.

(b) Home method with borax solution: dipping more effective than spray. See USDA leaflet cited on page 152.

Flammable. Ability of cotton and rayon fabrics, especially when napped, to support combustion. Inflammable—term no longer used. Wool blankets are recommended by fire insurance companies to smother fires. Their dense construction discourages burning.

Flannel. Plain or twill wool fabric slightly napped. May contain cotton or a synthetic in blends or mixtures. See Viyella® flannel. Made in various weights and finishes for men's and women's wear.

Flannelette. Soft, plain-woven cotton fabric, napped on one side, usually striped or printed. Used for shirting and bath-robes.

Flat crepe. Smoother than crepe de Chine. Filling yarns have less twist than true crepe yarns.

Flaw in cloth. Irregularity in the fabric due to an imperfect warp or filling yarn, or to an accident in the weaving operation. See Complaints on Merchandise, Fig. 107. See Float.

Flax. Bast fibers from stalk of fiber flax plant, *Linum usitatissimum.* See Linen.

Fleece. Entire coat of wool as sheared from the animal. Fleece wool means clipped, not pulled.

Fleece fabric. Characterized by soft woolen twill with deep nap for coatings; may be knitted.

Fleece lined.

(a) Usually knitted cotton with a nap on one side made into warm underwear.

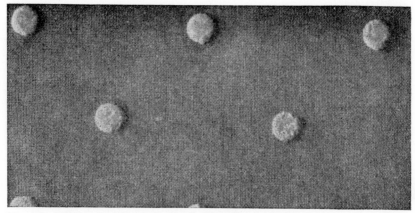

Fig. 23. Flock. Rayon flock printed on sheer cotton.

(b) Double-knit construction as cotton "sweat shirts" with loops on one or both sides.

Float. Flaw in cloth where a loose yarn "floats" on the surface. Yarns for decorative purposes may float from one design to another.

Flock.

(a) Fibers cut from rayon, cotton, wool, nylon from ½ mm. to 2 mm. in length. These cut fibers are anchored to base materials by various methods.

(b) Flock printing. Sheer cotton or rayon printed with flock to resemble weaving or embroidery, e.g., dotted Swiss. Fig. 23.

(c) Flock-covered fabrics have suede-like surface. Used for linings of cases.

Floss silk.

(a) Waste silk made into a bat for padding Japanese kimonos.

(b) Yarn made from spun silk slightly twisted, seen in Far Eastern embroideries.

Fluorescent dye. Brilliant colors used for luminosity on yarns and fabrics to be made into swim suits, sport coats, and trimmings. Day-glo®.

Forestry cloth. Made originally for U. S. Forest Service. Twilled flannel in "winter field shade" or olive drab for outing shirts and suits.

Formite®. Nonwoven rayon and cotton interfacing

Fortisan® rayon. High tenacity yarn. Fine, light, strong, supple yarns for draperies, sheer curtains, upholstery fabrics.

Fortrel® polyester. Similar to other polyesters in properties and end uses.

Fortuny print. Hand printed fabrics by Mariano Fortuny of Venice. Used for house furnishings and wearing apparel.

Foulard (foo-lard).

(a) Soft, lightweight, twill silk fabric always printed. Used for dresses, lingerie, neckties.

(b) Copied in rayon or cotton.

(c) Heavier weight for pajamas or curtains.

French crepe. Not a true crepe, originally silk. Rayon French crepe, so-called, is of plain weave and its yarn has no crepe twist. Used for lingerie or outer wear.

Frieze (freez). Originally made in Friesland, Holland. Heavy woolen twill overcoating, napped. Frieze called free-zay. See Frisé.

Frise (free-zay). The incorrect spelling "frieze" has been accepted as current. Pile fabric for upholstery or carpets with shallow uncut loops. Designs are produced by contrast of cut and uncut loops. May be made of mohair, wool, nylon, Acrilan® or mixtures.

Fuji silk. Japanese plain-woven spun silk in various weights. Copied in rayon.

Full fashioned. Hosiery and sweaters shaped in knitting.

Fulling. Finishing process on wool goods. A controlled amount of moisture shrinks the cloth, while heat sets it.

Fur fabrics. Pile weave of mohair, nylon, rayon, Dynel®, Orlon® or spun silk to imitate such furs as astrakhan, beaver, Persian lamb. Has distinctive curl; may be woven or knitted, often with a cotton back. Uses: coats, coat linings, trimmings, toys.

Gabardine.

(a) Worsted ply yarn, having a steep twill and warp face, for men's and women's wear, uniforms.

(b) Cotton, mercerized 2-ply yarn similar to above in appearance and uses.

(c) Wool, cotton, rayon, or nylon yarns combined or blended for similar uses.

(d) Stretch gabardine. Made of wool and nylon for ski pants; stretches lengthwise. Imported from Austria. Width: 60".

Gas-fading. Tendency of certain colors in acetate fabrics to fade or change color due to light or atmospheric gases; unless the material is treated to prevent this occurrence.

Gassing. Singeing of protruding fiber ends on cotton yarn or cloth by tiny gas flames. A smooth surface results.

Gauge (gage). Measure of fineness in knitting, also indicates thickness of plastics, coated fabrics, and linoleum.

Gauze (gah-z) weave.

(a) Another name for leno weave.

(b) Open, lacy fabrics often referred to as gauze.

Generic terms. Rayon, nylon, saran, or spandex (not capitalized) refer to a class of textile products not registered as trade marks. See Legislation.

Georgette. Thin, plain-weave silk, crepey fabric of S and Z twist yarns, alternating by twos. Used for women's wear.

Germantown. Worsted knitting yarn, 4-ply, slack twist.

Gerona®. A soft, rich looking woolen pile fabric, used for women's coats. Has a narrower and flatter pile than does Marvella®.

Gingham. Yarn-dyed plain woven cotton fabric in checks, plaids, stripes or plain colors. Better grades are made from combed yarns; lower grades, from carded yarn. Used to make clothing.

Fig. 24. Glenurquhart check. Tweed or suiting.

(a) Nurses' gingham. Heavy blue and white striped, closely woven.

(b) Tissue gingham. Thinner and more delicate than ordinary gingham; may be corded or have woven designs.

Glass. Generic term. See Legislation.

Glass toweling. Smooth linen, cotton, or union, made to be used for wiping glassware. May contain blended cotton and spun rayon.

Glass yarns. Woven into fabrics, as Fiber glass PPG. See Fiberglas®.

Glazed chintz or other fabrics. Durable treatment with resin compound. Example: Everglaze® finish. A nondurable finish is also called glazed, and is done with starch and friction.

Glenurquhart check. Name of pattern in suiting or tweed. Fig. 24. See District checks.

Glosheen®. High-grade sateen, used for draperies and women's wear. Vat-dyed, it may be plain or printed, also quilted.

Gobelins. See Tapestry.

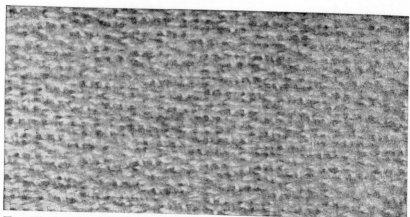

Fig. 25. Granite cloth. (See Momie.)

Granite cloth. Worsted fabric of hard-twist yarns in characteristic weave. Used for women's wear. Fig. 25.

Grass bleaching. Linens exposed on the grass to sun and air. No chemical is used. In Ireland it is called "crofting."

Grass cloth. See Ramie.

Gray goods. See Finishing.

Greige (gray-zh). Same as gray goods.

Grenadine. Sheer silk fabric of leno weave, used for dress goods.

Grenfell cloth. Plain, closely woven, water-repellent, windproof fabric made from Egyptian cotton for sportswear. Found in garments only, not yardage. Similar to Byrd cloth®.

Grosgrain (grow-grane). Firm, stiff, closely woven, plain corded fabric. The ribs are larger than those in faille. Made of silk, rayon, or nylon with cotton filling. Uses: ribbons, neckties.

Habutai (hab-u-tie). Plain-woven, lightweight Japanese silk originally made on hand looms. It is washable, usually white, and used for linings and dresses.

Haircloth.

    (a) Stiff, wiry fabric of cotton and horsehair used by tailors for interlining.

    (b) Furniture covering of a different texture.

Hair fibers. Called specialty hair fibers, and also fur fibers. Sources: alpaca, Angora goat (mohair), camel, Kashmir goat, vicuña. Often blended with wool.

Hand. Refers to "feel" of fabric, as soft, resilient, heavy, etc.

Hand blocked. Fabric which has been printed by hand with carved wood, linoleum or metal blocks.

The term *hand print* implies hand process. Used as equivalent of *screen print*.

Hand spun. Yarns spun by hand, less uniform than machine-spun yarns, and of more interesting texture. They are used in hand weaving and knitting.

Handkerchief linen. Sheer, plain weave linen fabric for women's handkerchiefs, lingerie. See Cambric.

Handwoven or hand-loomed. Exclusive fabrics produced by designers and weavers for draperies, upholstery, and garments. Fig. 26. See Fig. 1. Can be cleverly imitated by a machine process.

Hank. A large skein of yarn.

Hardanger cloth. Mercerized cotton in even basket weave for Norwegian Hardanger white embroidery.

Harris tweed®. Scotch wool, home spun, dyed, and hand woven by islanders on Harris and other outer Hebrides Islands. May be plain or twill for men's and women's outer wear.

Heat-sealing. Process of joining seams or parts of garment made of thermoplastic film by fusing the parts with heat instead of stitching.

Heat-setting. Stabilization of synthetic fabrics to insure no change in size or shape, as in nylon hose. Cotton fabrics also may be heat-set, using synthetic resins plus heat and pressure.

Heather mixture. Blend of colored wool fibers or yarns for tweeds. Suggests the color of a heather field in Scotland.

Heberlein®. The famous Swiss firm of this name is known for its permanently crisp finished organdy, and other fabrics and finishes. See Helanca®. Used under license by finishers.

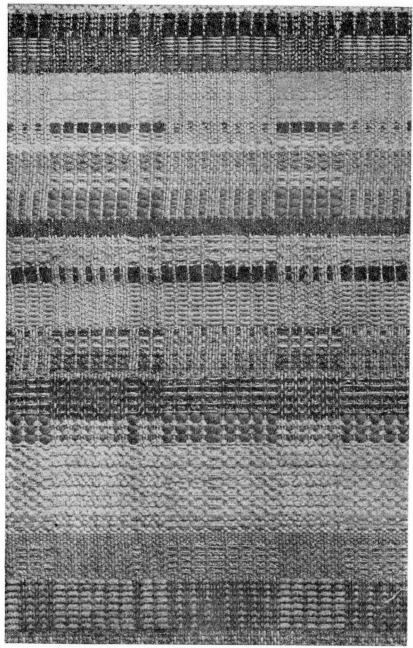

Fig. 26. Handwoven upholstery fabric, "Remoulade," by Jack Lenor Larsen. Warp: yarns of all fibers. Filling: linen yarn. Colors: yellows, oranges, and related hues.

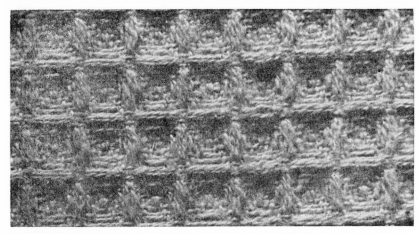

Fig. 27. Honeycomb or waffle weave (magnified). Coarse cotton drapery fabric.

Helanca®. High stretch nylon yarn, often combined with wool, and used for hosiery, swim suits, and other knit goods. May be of smooth or bouclé type.

Hemp. Fibers for rope and cordage. Abaca, sisal, and Manila hemp have largely replaced true hemp.

Herringbone twill. Same as Chevron. See Twill, Fig. 67.

Hickory stripe. Resembles express stripe. Material is used for work clothes. See Cottonade.

High tenacity rayon. Used in tire fabrics, for cargo chutes, and other industrial necessities. Some trade names are: Cordura®, Fortisan®, Tyrex®.

Homespun. Any fabric with rough, uneven weave which resembles hand weaving. Term used for wool suiting and cotton draperies.

Honan. Chinese fabric, narrow, lightweight, made of wild silk. Can be bleached.

Honeycomb and waffle weave. Type of figure weave in square ridges and hollows which suggest the surface of a honeycomb or waffle. Fig. 27. A variety of fabrics use this weave: wool baby blankets, cotton piqué, one type of cotton toweling, drapery fabrics, and wool coatings.

Hooked rug.

(a) Wool yarn or narrow strips of cloth hand-hooked into a canvas back.

(b) Machine imitation of above. See Chinese rug.

Hopsacking. Rough-textured basket weave in wool or various mixtures. Used for men's and women's suiting or coats.

Hosiery terminology.

(a) Women's hose in nylon are labelled according to size, gauge, and denier. They may be circular knit (seamless), full-fashioned, plain-knit, or of mesh construction, which resists runs. Come in various grades, as sheer, semi-sheer, service weight, etc. See Gauge.

(b) Support stockings are made of stretch nylon with cotton and nylon soles.

(c) Half hose, or socks, are seamless; yarns can be of any fiber or blend.

(d) Men's hose usually are of cotton, wool, or nylon, and are seamless. The ankle may be ribbed. Stretch yarn is used at top except in wool hose.

Hospital gauze. Very coarse cheesecloth for bandages, pads.

Hound's tooth. Pattern for one of the District checks in Scotland.

Huck. Toweling in characteristic weave. Fig. 28. Material may be linen, union or cotton; sometimes with rayon borders. Name may be woven in for hotels or hospitals.

Hydrophobic. Term for fibers which will not absorb water, as nylon, acrylic, and polyester fibers.

Hygroscopic property. Common to wool and silk which can retain more moisture than other fibers without seeming wet.

Iceland wool. Long lustrous hair from Iceland sheep, used for shawls and scarfs, usually hand-knitted; very lustrous, warm, and resilient.

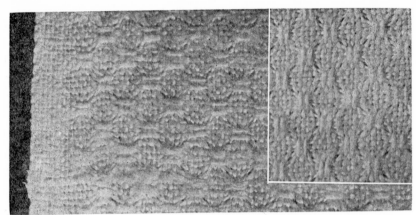

Fig. 28. Huck weave. Linen towel. Note reverse side.

Illusion. Another name for tulle, maline, or net of silk, rayon, or nylon.

Imitation leather. Vinyl products have largely replaced fabrics coated with pyroxylin. See Fabrilite®, Naugahyde®.

Imports. Use of textiles from abroad is growing. May be exclusive merchandise or low grade. Used for clothing, draperies, carpets, blankets, robes.

India linon. Term no longer used. Same as lawn.

India print. Hand-blocked cotton prints with native designs, in yardage or size for curtains, bedspreads.

Indian head®. Plain weave cotton; may be white, vat-dyed, or printed; with a smooth, durable finish. Has a wide usage: curtains, tablecloths, a variety of garments.

Indigo. Blue vegetable dye (the oldest vat dye) from the wood of a tropical tree. Now replaced by synthetic indigo.

Industrial fabrics. Wide variety used in various processes, as, cotton for buffing, filtering, conveyor belts, etc. Some synthetics are useful for chemical and oil filters.

Insect repellent. Various treatments of yarns or fabrics to render the material unwholesome to clothes moths, carpet beetles and silverfish. See Dieldrin.

Insulating materials.

(a) Nonwoven, foam type; Curon®, Scott Apparel Foam®. Laminated to knit or woven fabrics for warmth and lightness in garments for sports and travel. May substitute for interlining.

(b) Fiber foam, man-made, used in bats for quilting. See Dacron® fiberfill.

Interfacing fabrics. Material used between two layers of fabric as in collars, cuffs, buttonhole areas.

(a) Cotton: Super Siri®.

(b) Hair canvas: Armo®, is made of blends of wool, goat hair, cotton, rayon.

(c) Nonwoven material. Pellon®, Keybak®; resin-treated: Formite®, Interlon®, Pelomite®. Used also as lining to stiffen bouffant skirts.

See Insulating materials.

Interlining.

(a) Fabrics used between outer fabric and lining for added warmth. May be flannel or cotton, wool or other fibers, having a plain loose weave, usually napped on both sides.

(b) Quilted interlining made of carded wool, cotton, or other fibers, both sides covered with cheesecloth, or one with regular lining satin, may serve as lining or interlining. Sunbak®. See Quilted fabrics.

Interlon®. Nonwoven interfacing material of nylon and rayon. Washable, dry cleanable. Comes in different weights and widths.

Irish linen. Woven in Ireland; protected by trade names. Moygashel® is well known.

Jacquard (zha-kard).

(a) Elaborate woven patterns, as brocade and damask, done on a Jacquard loom; named for its inventor, J. M. Jacquard in 1801.

(b) Jacquard designs also in knit goods as sweaters.

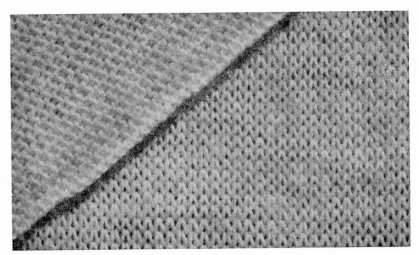

Fig. 29. Jersey. Cotton. Right side and reverse.

Jaspé (jas-pay). Features irregular, indistinct stripes, warp-wise. Same as Strié. Used for draperies and slipcovers.

Jean. Twilled cotton fabric, similar to drill, for sportswear and uniforms.

Jersey. Plain knitted, not ribbed, circular knit. Fig. 29. Made from yarns of any fiber, or blends. Wool jersey is usually tubular; Acetate, Arnel® triacetate, and nylon are cut and sold flat. Rayon or nylon jersey, if napped, is called matte. Worsted is produced in different weights and blends.

Jetspun®. Solution-dyed filament rayon.

Jute. Coarse brown fiber from the stalk of a plant in India. Used for burlap, cordage, and backings of rugs and carpets.

Kapok. Soft, delicate fibers from the seed pod of a tree in East and West Indies. Lighter than air; used for life preservers, pillows. Lacks durability.

Kasha. Fine, soft, napped wool dress goods—originated with Rodier Frères, France.

Kashmir. Hairs of a goat native to India. They are soft, silky, extremely fine. Kashmir shawls of India were made of silk warp with Kashmir filling. See Cashmere.

Kemp. Coarse wool or hair fibers shed from animals. Kempy wool is unsatisfactory for dyeing.

Kenisan®. Durable treatment of cotton goods to retard growth of bacteria and/or fungi.

Kersey. Thick, woolen twilled cloth related to Melton or heavy broadcloth but having a shorter nap. Uses: uniforms, overcoats.

Keybak®. Bonded fabric made for interfacing and interlining; in form of net for ventilation; of nylon and other fibers. Launders, dry cleans, holds shape. Also used to make towels, for filtration and for other industrial applications.

Khaki (kah-ky). Name of a color; Hindu word for "dusty." Fabric of this distinctive color in cotton; used for uniforms of servicemen and Boy Scouts and for sportswear.

Knit goods. Fabric constructed by interlooping of yarns in a continuous mesh. Advantages of knit goods: elastic, warm, nonwrinkling.

   (a) Hand knitting. Made by slipping stitches from one needle to another and making new stitches with each change.

   (b) Knitted pile fabric. Made when two yarns, one of which has longer loops, are left as loops, as in sweat shirts, or sheared, napped, or brushed. Swiss velour (imported) is all cotton; its surface has a rich velvety texture.

   (c) Jacquard patterns, as in ski sweaters, are produced on a machine similar in principle to the Jacquard loom for pattern weaving.

Knitting—machine types.

   (a) Circular or weft: the simplest knit structure. Used in seamless hose. See Jersey.

   (b) Double knit. Double faced. Originated in Italy.

   (c) Flat knit. Yarns travel forth and back across the knitting frame. By increasing or decreasing the number of loops, full-fashioned hose or sweaters are shaped.

(d) Raschel. Flat, warp-knit fabric. Variety of effects, including lace and net, may be produced. See Rovana® saran.

(e) Rib knit. Rib knitting is more elastic than plain (jersey) or warp knit.

(f) Warp knit. Least elastic of all knit types. See Milanese. See Tricot. Method is used to make the run-resistant fabric used in gloves.

Kodel® (kod-el) **polyester fiber.** Made into yarns and fabrics which are crease and pleat retentive, resistant to pilling, quick drying, and need little or no pressing. Blends with cotton and other natural and man-made fibers. Uses: men's, women's, children's clothing.

Koroseal®.

(a) Vinyl plastic alone or on cotton base, used for upholstery, wall covering. Varies in gauge, colors, and textures.

(b) Unsupported film used for rainwear, shower curtains, play ponds, and to cover tobacco fields.

Kroy®. Treatment of wool, previous to spinning, to prevent shrinkage in knit goods, such as men's hosiery.

Lace. Originally made by hand with bobbins (bobbin or pillow lace) or needle (needlepoint). Machine reproductions imitate handmade lace in narrow widths for trimmings or wide widths for dresses.

Lace fabric. Machine-made by twisting threads about each other to simulate handmade lace which is in limited demand. May be made of cotton, rayon, nylon or Orlon®. See Filet. See Lace. Used for curtains, tablecloths, bedspreads; made up in yardage for dresses, blouses. Also, narrow lace is made for trimmings. See Net. See Burnt-out process.

Lacelon® acetate ribbon. See Ribbon. Fig. 30. Lacy bands, treated for water repellency, used in florists' trade and for gift wrapping. Comes 3″ wide in 30 yd. rolls.

Lacquer finish. Chemical treatment which produces a thin

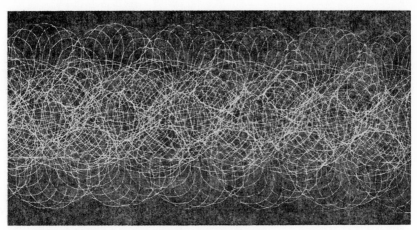

Fig. 30. Lacelon®. Nonwoven acetate ribbon.

film on the surface of cloth. May be applied in color for design. Usually not dry cleanable.

Lamb's wool. Finer and softer than ordinary sheep's wool. See Shetland.

Lamé (Fr., "leaves of gold or silver"; pr. lam-may). Originally, rich silk fabric brocaded in silver or gold. Modern lamé uses aluminum foil to simulate cloth of gold or silver. It may also be enhanced by woven designs. See Metallic cloth.

Lamé®. Nontarnishable metallic yarns made in various colors and sizes.

Laminated fabric.
   (a) Two or more layers of cloth fused together as for men's shirt collars and women's fabric belts.
   (b) Waterproof paper and cloth are laminated to make shipping bags.
   (c) Fabric foam is laminated by thermal or wet adhesive method. See Curon®, Scott Apparel Foam®.

Lampas. Drapery or upholstery fabric similar to brocade. May be of any combination of yarns, usually having two sets of warp and filling yarns.

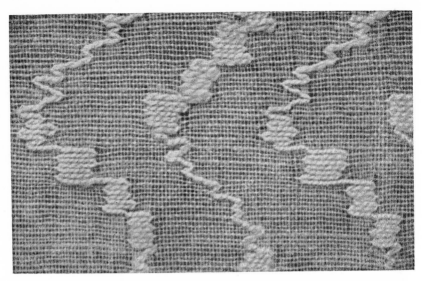

Fig. 31. Lappet weave (magnified).

Lanaset®. Finish for wool to set and control its shrinkage.

Lanella®. Swiss product; lightweight flannel; blend of half cotton and half wool.

Lappet. Woven design usually made on sheer cotton with extra warp yarns, heavier than the ground fabric, zig-zagged across the warp in weaving, which produces an embroidery-like effect. Fig. 31. Dots or small figures may be made, but clipped spots are less expensive.

Lastex®. Elastic yarn made by wrapping textile yarns or fibers around a core of rubber or spandex fiber. May be woven or knitted for hosiery, swim suits or intimate apparel.

Lawn. Thin, lightweight, plain-woven cotton of carded or combed yarns, with either a soft or stiff finish. Used for linings, handkerchiefs, women's wear. Was formerly called India linon. This term and linene are considered misleading because the fabrics contain no linen.

Leno. Type of weave in which warp yarns, arranged in pairs,

Fig. 32. Leno weave. Marquisette, Fiberglas®.

twist about each other between rows of filling. Fig. 32. See Marquisette.

Liberty®. Wide range of fabrics by English manufacturer, particularly prints of exclusive designs on cotton, silk or sheer wool.

Line. Long flax fibers separated from short ones, called tow.

Linen. Yarn, thread, or fabric made from flax fibers.

Linen canvas. Interfacing for tailors' use.

Linen tester. See Testing—Thread count.

Linen-textured. Cotton, silk, or rayon woven of rough yarns which suggest the surface of crash. It resembles texture of linen. Incorrect to call it silk linen.

Linings.

(a) For dresses, to protect from skin and to preserve shape of skirts. May be plain cotton as lawn, crinoline; silk or nylon; organza, taffeta.

(b) For suits and coats, to afford warmth and smooth surface in wear; many fabrics as satin, sateen, crepe, taffeta, twill in silk, rayon, acetate, Arnel® triacetate.

(c) Fleeceback satin. See Sunback®.

(d) Metal coated or reflective lining. See Milium®.

See Interfacing. See Interlining.

Linon (Fr., "lawn"). See Lawn.

Linters. Short cotton fibers which adhere to the seeds after the first ginning. Used for manufacture of rayon, for insulation, and for stuffing in upholstery. Inferior to cotton staple for mattresses.

Lisle (lie-l). Hardspun, 2-ply, long staple, combed cotton. Used chiefly in hosiery, fabric gloves, and underwear.

Loden cloth. Originally Austrian, although now it is made in several countries. Thick-woven wool, softer than Melton, used for outer wear—especially ski clothing. Different textures are called Loden cloth.

Loft. Refers to deep nap on a blanket or the soft, spongy feel of a highly napped sweater.

London-shrunk. Process used by tailors for wool goods. A cold water treatment, it involves drying and pressing.

Longcloth. Lightweight, plain-woven, unfinished, bleached muslin used for underwear and linings. See Nainsook.

Long staple.

(a) Wool fibers of length suitable for combing.

(b) Cotton fibers, especially Egyptian or sea island; length 1⅛″ to 2½″.

Lorganza®. Originated by Bianchini Férier, Inc. Pure silk, sheer, plain weave; slightly stiff because of silk gum. Uses: formals, linings.

Lumarith®. Transparent plastic sheet form made from acetate rayon. See Cellophane.

Luminescence. Treatment of fabrics to make them visible after light has been withdrawn. Used for theatrical costumes, signs, and safety devices. See Fluorescent dye.

Lumite®. Fabric woven of plastic yarns to be used as insect screen cloth, automobile seat-cover fabrics, outdoor furniture fabrics.

Lurex®. Metallic yarns are laminations of clear plastic films and aluminum foil or metallized film. Washable, dry cleanable, and nontarnishable.

Lustering. Finishing process by heat and pressure to produce luster on yarns or cloth.

Lycra® spandex. Multifilament; strong, lightweight stretch yarn, used in foundation garments and swimsuits. See Vyrene®.

Macintosh®. Originally, the waterproof method of treating fabric discovered by Charles Macintosh. Spelled also Mackintosh.

Name applies to fine poplin made water-repellent; label used on raincoats.

Mackinaw. Heavy, woolen twill, napped; may have plaid back (double cloth). Used for windbreakers, overcoats.

Madras. Origin, India; used for sailors' head-dresses.

   (a) Imported handwoven cotton stripes or plaids for bed-spreads and curtains. Fast color label.

   (b) No longer made in Madras. Imitated by machine-woven.

   (c) So-called "bleeding madras" for sportswear shirts; usually plaid design. Label says "guaranteed to bleed." Colors blend after washing.

   (d) Shirting. Soft cotton fabric, having a woven design, or checks, or cords, mercerized and Sanforized®, white or colors.

Maline (mah-leen). Fine, stiff net of silk, nylon, or rayon for veils, millinery trimmings. See Illusion. See Tulle.

Manila hemp. Not true hemp. See Abaca. Obtained from the fleshy leaves of plant stalks. Fabric is not woven in the United States.

Man-made fibers. Those fibers used for textile purposes which do not occur in nature. Many products being developed in

Fig. 33. Matelassé.

Europe, South America, Japan, and Canada. See Synthetic filaments.

Marquisette. Open fabric, leno weave, of mercerized cotton, rayon, Dacron®, Orlon® or Fiberglas®. May have woven dots or figures; also clipped dots, Fig. 14. Comes with many variations in texture. Leno, Fig. 32. Uses: glass curtains, dresses.

Martinized®. Durable crush-resistant finish on velvet; product of one firm.

Marvella®. Soft, rich-looking woolen pile fabric, used for women's coats; and having a wider wale pile than Gerona®.

Masslinn®. Nonwoven fabric of rayon, cotton, and other fibers, used for disposable napkins, towels, dust and polishing cloths, and casket linings.

Matelasse (mat-las-say). A kind of weave, usually Jacquard, producing a quilted or padded texture. Imitation matelassé is not woven, but stitched or embossed. Fig. 33.

Matt or matte. Dull or delustered man-made fiber or yarn; example: matt jersey.

Mechanical fabrics. Large class of fabrics, such as cotton, for laundry supply trade; nylon and rayon for tire fabrics; Fiberglas® for insulation, both electrical and thermal. See Industrial fabrics.

Melton. Thick, smooth, woolen twill, heavier than broadcloth or Kersey, resembles felt. Has a short nap, and a dull finish. Uses: uniforms, overcoats, sportswear. See Loden cloth.

Meraklon®️ polypropylene. Versatile low-cost fiber of Italian origin. Many uses. Its application in the United States is at the experimental stage.

Mercerized. A physical and chemical process which renders cotton permanently more lustrous, stronger, more absorbent, more susceptible to dye, and makes it hold color better than natural cotton. The yarn or cloth is treated with caustic soda under tension. See Durene®.

Merino.
 (a) Name of a breed of sheep.
 (b) In knit goods may refer only to all wool.

Merinova®. See Protein fibers.

Merinova®️ azlon. Protein fiber manufactured in Italy; used in making felts.

Mesh fabric. Open knit construction for undershirts, sweaters, mesh gloves, or hose; also in leno or basket weave for men's summer shirts.

Metallic. Generic term. See Legislation.

Metallic cloth. Fabrics of any material, woven or knitted, with metallic yarn added to give brilliance. Uses: women's clothing and draperies. See Lamé®, Lurex®, Metlon®, Mylar®, Reymet®.

Metallic print. Pattern printed with lacquer and coated with pulverized gold, silver, or copper mixed with a binder, usually on cotton or rayon. Not always dry cleanable.

Metlon®. Metallic yarn, made of bright aluminum foil laminated between two plies of plastic film; nontarnishing. Also Metlon® with Mylar® polyester fiber.

Milanese (mill-a-nees). Type of run-resistant warp-knit fabric with diagonal cross effect on the back made of silk, rayon, and nylon; used for gloves and lingerie.

Mildew resistant. Chemical treatment on cotton to retard growth of bacteria and fungi. See Sanitized®.

Milium®. Insulating lining fabric made of satin, taffeta, or twill, in acetate and/or rayon, or cotton which gives warmth without weight. The reverse side of the material is coated with a resinous binder generally containing metallic flakes. This surface reflects body heat. Used in women's coats, also in drapery lining for insulating purposes.

Mill ends. Remnants or short lengths from the mill.

Mineral fibers. From sources in the earth as asbestos; silica, for glass fibers.

Mitin® (mitt-in). Chemical process for mothproofing wool; blankets, apparel, hand knit yarns. Washable, durable.

Mixtures. Term used rather loosely to define fabrics of two or more fibers. Yarns often are combined, as cotton warp and wool filling in checks and plaids. Fabrics containing blended yarns should be referred to as blends. See Blends.

Modacrylic. Generic term. See Legislation.

Mohair fabrics. See Angora goat.

(a) Mohair in blends and mixtures with cotton, rayon, or nylon is used for drapery or upholstery. Comes in various weaves.

(b) In making coating it is usually combined with other fibers.

(c) Pile fabric, having a cotton back and a cut or uncut pile is used for toys and upholstery especially in public conveyances. Rayon or nylon pile are sometimes substitutes.

Moire (mwar-ay). Pattern produced with engraved rollers, heat, and pressure on corded silk, cotton, or rayon; usually a watered design. Fig. 34. Plastic embossing on cotton, or heat embossing on acetate rayon, are durable through washing.

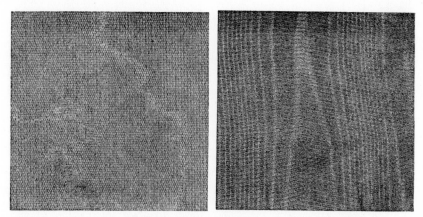

Fig. 34. Moiré. All silk drapery fabric (left). Acetate (right).

Scratch moiré refers to any design other than the conventional watered effect.

Moisture regain. Yarn or fabric after exposure to standard atmosphere at relative humidity 65 per cent (± 2) and temperature 70° F. ($\pm 2°$) as compared with its oven-dry weight.

Moleskin. Heavy cotton, filling-face satin weave; napped on the back. Used for sport coats and as a base for imitation leather and adhesive plaster.

Momie (mummy). Irregular weave, producing rough pebbly surface. May be linen, cotton, or a mixture. If wool, called granite cloth. See Granite cloth.

Momme (mummy). Japanese unit of weight for pongee and habutai.

Monk's cloth. Rough canvas-like cotton in basket weave 2-2 and 4-4. May be natural color, or have dyed or woven stripes; used for curtains and wall coverings. See Figs. 2 and 3.

Monofilament. Coarse viscose rayon, nylon, or saran resembling horsehair; woven into braids and sewn to make women's hats; also automobile upholstery fabric. A monofilament is not a yarn; one filament is used as the weaving element.

Mordant. Chemical used on textile fibers, yarns, or cloth to increase their affinity for dye. Dyes requiring a mordant such as logwood are called mordant dyes.

Mosquito net. Coarse cotton, leno weave, heavily sized, white green, or black; having a barred effect produced by thick yarns. Used for canopies on beds and makeshift window screens.

Moth repellency. Chemical treatment of wool products to make them impervious to attacks of moths and carpet beetles. Mitin®. Mill treatment indicated on blankets and rugs. Many products are on the market for home application. DDT spray is also much used.

Mousseline de soie (moss-sa-leen de-swa). Means silk muslin, a fabric stiffer than voile, also called starched chiffon.

Moygashel (moy-gash'-el). Irish linen dress and suit fabric, finished for wrinkle resistance.

Moynel® polynosic. See Zantrel® polynosic.

Multifilament. A number of filaments twisted together to make yarn. See Monofilament.

Muslin. Origin in ancient city of Mosul. Firm, plain-woven cotton, stronger and heavier than longcloth, coarser than cambric. Bleached and unbleached. Many uses. See Sheeting. Sheer fabric, plain or printed, called muslin in England.

Mylar® polyester. Film made into metallic yarn by laminating and slitting. Yarns are soft, washable, nontarnishing. These decorative yarns can be woven or knitted.

Nainsook. Lightweight, soft, plain-woven cotton; may be mercerized or schreinerized. Comes in white, pastel, or print, for infants' wear, lingerie, or blouses. See Longcloth.

Napery (nay-pary). General term for tablecloths and napkins of either linen or cotton.

Napping. Finishing process as for wool, broadcloth, cotton, outing flannel, or knit goods. The ends of fibers are raised to the surface by revolving cylinders covered with metal teeth or teasel burrs. Not to be confused with pile. See Brushed knit fabrics.

Narco® viscose. Rayon yarns in various deniers, spun by the spool process. End uses include an extensive range of apparel fabrics. Product of one company.

Natural fibers. Those textile fibers that occur in nature. Plant sources: cellulosic; cotton, flax, abaca, jute, ramie, etc.
Animal sources: wool, hair, silk, fur. See Man-made fibers.

Naugahyde® (naw-ga-hide). Vinyl upholstery material in various colors, weights, textures. Used also for wall covering.

Net. All nets and laces were first made by hand with a needle or with bobbins. Machine-made nets simulate the originals.

   (a) The bobbinet type may be cotton, silk, nylon, or Orlon® for curtains and linings. Finer grades are made for dresses and trimmings.

   (b) Blond net. Originally white, term now little used.

   (c) Bobbinet hexagonal mesh.

Ninon (nee-non). Plain, sheer, crisp fabric usually acetate for curtains and evening wear.

Noils. Short fibers of wool, rayon, silk, or nylon. They are the by-product of manufacturing processes.

Nonrun. In women's hose a device below the welt to stop runs.

Nonwoven fabrics. See Bonded fabrics.

   (a) Wide variety of disposable materials which serve for towels, napkins, diapers, aprons, shower slippers; surgical and industrial uses. Masslinn® is made by one company.

   (b) Durable interlinings and interfacings. See Pellon®, Interlon®, Pelomite®.

   (c) Cellulose acetate products. See Lacelon®, Sasheen®.

   (d) Felt. See Feutron®.
   Fiber content varies according to use. See Insulating materials.

Norane®. Water repellent treatment for rainwear, boys' outer clothing.

Novelty weaves. Not fundamental weaves. Any combination of techniques such as dobby.

Fig. 35. Novelty yarns. Left to right: (1) corkscrew, (2) gimp, (3) knot or spot, (4) slub, (5) loop.

Novelty yarns. For weaving and knitting by hand or machine. Class includes a variety of fibers, blends, constructions such as corkscrew, gimp, knot, slub, loop. See Yarns, novelty, Fig. 35.

Numdah. Felt rug made in India of goats' hair, embroidered with colored yarns in chain stitch.

Nun's veiling. Lightweight, plain weave fabric, similar to voile but closer and softer, in worsted or silk. Made originally in black for nuns' veils; may be white or dyed for dresses, négligées.

Nurses' cloth. Stiff, plain weave white cotton with linen finish, used for nurses' uniforms.

Nylon. Generic term. See Legislation.

Nylon. Generic term for large class of synthetic products having various forms and uses. Textile yarns in filament, staple, plain or crimped fibers; bright or dull. Used alone or in blends.

Properties: high tensile strength, resistance to abrasion, non-absorbency, high melting point, heat-setting property.

Widespread uses in hosiery, knit garments, woven goods for lingerie and dresses. Extensive use for industrial purposes.

See Nymo®. See Stretch yarns.

Nylon 6-6, name given regular filament.

Nylon 6. Designed for specific end uses as carpet yarn, tire fabrics, upholstery.

Nylon thread. Made by two constructions: the conventional twisted filaments have a tendency to kink; those made by the monocord process, such as Nymo® bonded filaments, will not kink.

Nymo®. See Nylon thread.

Nytril. Generic term. See Legislation.

Odor-resistant. Chemical treatment of cloth for germ or odor resistance. Applied to canvas shoes, shoe linings, mattress covers, powder puffs. Sanitized®, Kenisan®.

Off-grain. Defect in printed goods when design does not follow filling yarns. Refers to error in cutting of garment. "Off-grain," is not on the thread. See Complaints on Merchandise.

Oilcloth. Oldest coated fabric. Has a cotton base with coating of linseed oil and pigments, and is finished in various ways. Plain or printed, for table covers, book covers, and bags.

Oiled silk. Thin silk treated with boiled linseed oil making it waterproof and pliable, for surgical uses, shower curtains. Largely replaced by plastic film.

Olefin. Generic term. See Legislation.

Olefin. Yarns made by various companies. Fabrics for home furnishing, industrial uses, and apparel.

Olive drab. Called OD; color for uniforms. See Khaki.

Organdy.

    (a) Thin, transparent, stiff, plain cotton of fine combed yarns. Better grades, Swiss imports, have a durable crisp finish.

    (b) Nylon organdy resembles cotton in texture.

    (c) Shadow organdy is pigment-printed, to show opaque designs. Uses: dresses, blouses, curtains.

Organza. Silk organdy, plain weave, stiff; comes in white and colors; used for formals and linings. Hand washable. May be of rayon or nylon.

Sometimes confused with Lorganza®.

Oriental rugs. Made by hand, not on a power loom, in any part of the Orient. Principal sources: Persia (Iran); India (many with modern designs); Turkey; Morocco (native designs).

Orlon® acrylic. Filament or staple form. Properties of Orlon® fabrics with filament yarns: silkiness, light weight, high tensile strength, heat-setting ability. They are also resistant to sunlight and atmospheric gases, easy to launder, quick drying, and resistant to mildew, moths, pilling, shrinkage, and chemicals, particularly acids.

(a) Staple is resilient, warm, bulky, and requires special dyes. Uses: awnings, industrial fabrics, apparel, especially coats.

(b) Orlon® is often blended with wool, cotton or rayon. Uses: sweaters, blankets, fleece coats. See Acrilan® acrylic, Dynel® modacrylic.

Orlon® cantrece®. Filament acrylic yarn textured fiber used in lightweight silklike sweaters which retain their shape, and need no stretching or blocking.

Osnaburg. Coarse cotton cloth first made for grain and cement sacks. Plain weave, made of carded yarns, natural or unbleached; dyed or printed for draperies and apparel.

Ottoman. Heavy corded silk, rayon, or nylon with cotton cord filling; characterized by broad flat ribs alternating with smaller ribs for women's coats and trimmings.

Outing flannel. Old name: domett. Soft, lightweight cotton, plain or twill, napped on both sides. Soils readily, nap wears and washes off. Flammable unless treated. Comes in white, solid colors, with a yarn-dyed stripe, or printed. Used for sleeping garments and interlinings.

Oxford. Group of cotton fabrics; made of combed yarn, having a modified basket weave, and used chiefly for shirtings. Sailcloth is also modified basket weave.

Oxford gray. Mixture of black and white wool fibers in ply yarns for woven or knitted goods.

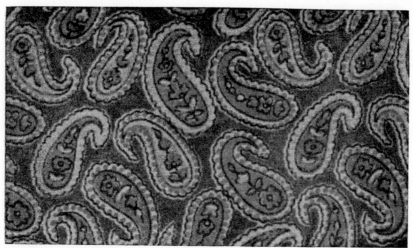

Fig. 36. Paisley print. On sheer cotton voile.

Painted fabrics. Some fabrics are painted freehand in exclusive patterns.

Paisley print. Fig. 36. Design printed on any fabric to imitate original shawl pattern. See Paisley shawl.

Paisley shawl. The original ones were handwoven in Paisley, Scotland to imitate Kashmir shawls of India. The characteristic design is copied in woven, knitted, and printed fabrics.

Pajama check. Barred nainsook for men's underwear. Heavier than dimity. Characterized by groups of yarns, rather than cords as in dimity.

Palm beach®. Lightweight fabric having cotton warp and mohair filling. Also may be blends of mohair, rayon, cotton or nylon. Uses: Play wear, suiting for men's wear.

Peau de soie (Fr., "skin of silk"; pr. po-da-swah).

(a) Pure silk material, flat, having a riblike filling, very close weave, and a rich, smooth feel. When squeezed, it becomes crumpled but can be smoothed out with the hand.

(b) Copied in acetate and blends, which are of lighter weight. Many variations known as peau de soie.

Pellon®. Nonwoven interfacing whose fiber content varies according to end use. It has a feltlike texture, is washable, dry cleanable and comes in different weights. Used for stiffening skirts and for inner soles of shoes.

Pelomite®. Nonwoven interfacing made of rayon and other fibers. May be fused to other fabrics with a hot iron. See Insulating materials.

Percale. Cotton with a plain weave, may be white, solid color, or printed. Better grades sold by thread count 80 x 80. See Sheets—percale.

Permacel®. See Tapes.

Permanent finish. Term used in the trade but disapproved by Federal Trade Commission. Durable is preferred.

Permel Plus®. Process making fabrics crease and soil resistant as well as water-repellent and washable. Permel ® used by one company as prefix to various other finishes. See Cyana®.

Pick. Individual filling yarns for weaving.

Picot (pee-ko). Small loop woven on edge of ribbon or loop on lace.

Piece-dyed. See Dyeing.

Pigmenting. Process of giving permanent dullness to rayons. A finely divided pigment, titanium dioxide, is added to the spinning solution before yarns are spun. See Pigment print.

Pigment print. Printed with a chemical which gives opaque pattern; may be self color or contrasting. Fig. 37.

Pile fabrics. See Pile weave, Fur fabrics, Plush, Velvet, Velveteen.
    Fig. 38. Pile fabric, construction.
    Fig. 39. Pile fabric, mohair, loops.
    Fig. 40. Pile rug, cotton, loops.
    Fig. 41. Pile rug, cut and uncut loops.

Pile weave. Raised loops, cut or uncut, which form part or all of the surface in pile fabrics. See Terry.

Fig. 37. Pigment print on Fortisan® rayon and silk drapery fabric; white on white.

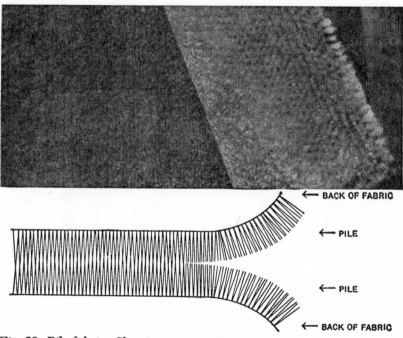

← BACK OF FABRIC

← PILE

← PILE

← BACK OF FABRIC

Fig. 38. Pile fabric. Showing construction.

Fig. 39. Pile fabric for upholstery. Mohair loops.

Pilling. Formation of little balls of fibers called "pills" produced by wear on the surface of woven or knitted garments. Occurs when short fibers are used.

Pima (pee-ma) cotton. Originally, long staple cotton fibers from Pima County Arizona; used in combed yarns for fine dress goods and shirtings. Pima is often used to refer to long staple cotton from Peru and Egypt. See SuPima®.

Fig. 40. Pile rug. Cotton, uncut loops.

Fig. 41. Pile rug. Hand woven. Contemporary design, cut and uncut wool loops.

Piña (pee-nya). Thin, transparent, and stiff fabric made from pineapple fiber in the Philippine Islands. Not sold in American stores. See Structural fibers.

Piqué (pee-kay). Cotton fabric with warpwise cord effect; lighter in weight than Bedford cord. May be either pin wale or wide wale cord woven of carded or combed yarns, usually mercerized. Piqué, eyelet embroidery, Fig. 42.

(a) Bird's-eye woven pattern. Fig. 43 (right).

(b) Embossed resin pattern as bird's-eye. Fig. 43 (left).

(c) Novelty or matelassé piqué.

Plaid. Fabrics using warp and filling of colors to weave design. May be wool, cotton, rayon, nylon, or silk. Plaid may be copied in a print, as percale. See Tartan.

Plain knit. Found in hosiery and jersey cloth. Characterized by a distinct right and wrong side. Fig. 29.

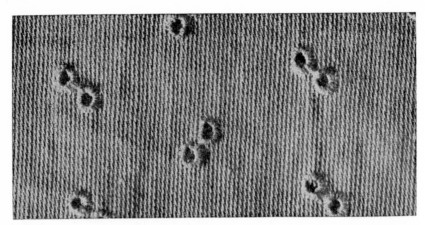

Fig. 42. Piqué. Eyelet embroidery.

Plain weave. Simplest of fundamental weaves. Called 1-1 or tabby; example, voile. Variations of plain weave are the rib and the basket. See Square weave, Fig. 44. Spaced warps, Fig. 45.

Plastic goods.

(a) Material produced by synthesis from sources similar to those of man-made fibers. May be used in sheet form, or as

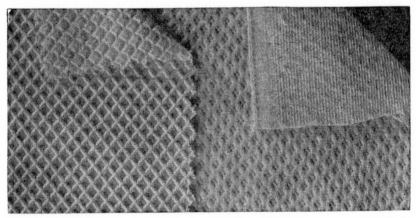

Fig. 43. Piqué. Bird's-eye pattern. Embossed (left), woven (right).

Fig. 44. Plain weave. Square. Reconstruction.

coated yarns or fabrics. Used for raincoats, upholstery, and
industrial purposes. See Ticking.

(b) Large class in industrial field not related to textiles.

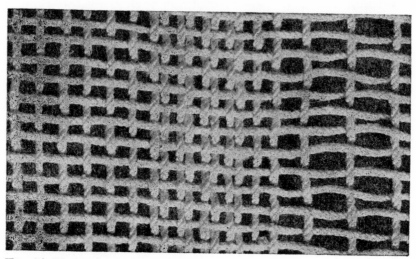

Fig. 45. Plain weave. Spaced warps. Reconstruction.

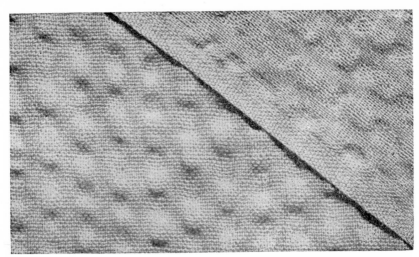

Fig. 46. Plissé. Cotton (Magnified).

Plated. Knit goods with face of one kind of yarn, such as worsted, and with back of another, as cotton. The principle is similar to plated silverware; the more expensive material usually appears on the surface. Applies to knitted fabrics only.

Pliofilm®. Plastic in sheet form, made in different gauges and colors, for use in making bags and other kinds of packaging.

Plissé (plee-say).

(a) Cotton with alternating plain and puckered stripes, formed by the shrinking action of caustic soda. Untreated portion has blistered effect. Comes in white, colors, and printed. Uses: blouses, dresses, and uniforms. Incorrectly called "plissé crepe," not a crepe. Fig. 46.

(b) Nylon plissé is similar in appearance, but its shrinkage is due to heat.

Plush. Cut-pile fabric having a pile of greater depth than that of velvet, usually 1/7″ or more. Name plush little used. See Fur fabrics.

(a) Mohair pile is usually made with a cotton back.

(b) Silk or wild silk pile is used for trimmings, muffs, caps.

(c) Rayon plush comes in various textures to imitate fur; used as covering for animal toys and for trims on coats.

Ply.

(a) Single yarns twisted together form ply-yarn, such as 2-ply. Many plies make a cord.

(b) One of several layers of a fabric as 3-ply cotton, used for shirt collars.

Poiret (pwa-ray) twill. Named for French dress designer Paul Poiret. Steep twill weave, worsted, resembles gabardine, but is finer and smoother.

Polished cotton. Describes cotton goods having a smooth finish. Usually has satin weave. The finish may be permanent or merely the result of a high calendering process to imitate cotton satin.

Polka dot. Round dots, embroidered, printed, or flock dots of any size forming a pattern. If very large, called coin dot.

Polo® cloth. Heavyweight coating fabric finished on both sides with dense nap. Usually tan color. May be all wool, all camel hair, or blends.

Polyester. Generic term. See Legislation.

Polynosic. Coined word (*poly*–"many"; *nosic*–"fibrils"). Generic classification for a type of regenerated cellulosic fiber. See Zantrel®, Moynel® polynosic.

Pongee. Corruption of two Chinese words which signify "native color."

(a) Pongee was originally woven on hand looms from wild silk.

(b) Domestic pongee imitates genuine pongee. May be of mercerized cotton, rayon, or spun silk. See Shantung.

Poplin. Ribbed fabric having a plain weave.

(a) Cotton, usually mercerized, white or piece-dyed for men's shirts, nurses' uniforms, dresses, and curtains.

(b) Silk, rayon, or nylon, usually with heavy filling yarns of worsted or cotton used for women's wear.

(c) Worsted fabric of same weave for dresses and suits.

Powder puff®. Fine cotton goods with starchless finish, smooth and crisp.

Preshrunk. Term used to indicate that a wool fabric has undergone a preshrinking process. See London-shrunk.

Print. General term for various fabrics especially cottons. See India print, Liberty print.

Printing. Method of stamping a pattern with dye on warp or fabric with a wood block or an engraved steel roller. See Blotch print.

Direct print: See Roller printing.

Discharge print: See Discharge print.

Duplex print: See Duplex print.

Hand blocked: See Hand blocked.

Photographic: Picture printed on sensitized cloth instead of paper.

Pigment: See Pigment print.

Resist: same principle as Batik.

Screen or stencil method: See Screen print.

Warp print: See Warp print.

Protein fibers. See Natural fibers; Animal sources.

Man-made: Azlon; generic term for any regenerated, naturally occurring protein as Ardil®, made from peanuts, a British product; Lanital® made from casein of milk, of Italian origin; and Merinova®, Italian import. They have many of the characteristics of wool, and are used chiefly in felting operations. Vicara fibers are made from Zein (zee-in) protein from corn. No longer made in the United States.

Pulled wool. Taken from pelts of dead animals by chemical means. Considered inferior to sheared wool.

Quilted. Two layers of cloth, enclosing sheet wadding or other stuffing, stitched together as in quilts. Imitated in weaving. See Matelassé.

Ramie (ram-my). Ancient Malayan word rami (pr. rah-mee). Fiber similar to flax is obtained from stalk of a plant grown in

Japan chiefly, but now also in the United States. The fabric is called grass cloth and is used for tea cloths and runners, also apparel.

Ramona®. Plain weave cotton, comes in white and a variety of fast-dyed colors, used for garments and many household uses. Woven 54″ wide for tablecloths. Resembles Indian head®.

Ratiné (ra-tee-nay). Loosely woven fabric, with a rough-appearing plain weave, and spongy feel. This texture is due to the nubby yarns. May be of cotton, wool, silk, rayon, or mixtures. Used for women's wear. Term little used.

Raw fibers.

(a) Textile fibers in their natural state as silk in the gum, and cotton as it comes from the boll.

(b) Raw silk. Term used incorrectly for any rough-textured silk. Actually, silk spun from wild silk cocoons.

Rayon. Name adopted in 1924 to replace "artificial silk" or "fiber silk." First commercially made synthetic fiber. Composed of regenerated cellulose.

(a) Original types: viscose and cuprammonium.

(b) Variations in form: continuous filament; or staple fibers cut for spinnable length; either smooth or crimped.

(c) Degrees of brightness or dullness.

(d) Size or fineness: see Denier.

(e) Characteristics of rayon fabrics: they react toward chemicals and dyes as do natural vegetable fibers. See Tests: Burning, Chemical. They are weakened when wet, but regain strength on drying; they tend to muss unless treated for crease resistance. They imitate other fibers; are used extensively as blends with cotton, wool, silk or other synthetics. See Avisco®, Bemberg®; high tenacity rayon as Cordura®.

(f) Viscose rayon. New properties have been developed; modified viscose types are made for specific end uses. See Avril®, Avlin®; Corval® and Topel®, cross-linked; Zantrel® polynosic.

Rayon. Generic term. See Legislation.

Reeled silk. Silk filaments wound directly from several cocoons into skeins; result is raw silk with no twist.

Reevon® olefin. Monofilament yarn.

Regain. Accepted moisture allowance for textiles expressed in percentage of their dry weight. See Conditioning.

Regenerated cellulose. See Rayon.

Rep or repp. Resembles poplin but has a heavier cord or filling, and is usually a wider fabric. May have a wool, silk, rayon, cotton, or nylon warp or the typical cotton one. Slub yarn from filling gives variety in texture. Chiefly used for drapery material, upholstery, and lighter weight suits and coats.

Reprocessed wool. Wool fibers previously woven or knitted but never used by a consumer. Wool is reduced to the fibrous state, respun, and woven. Is the same as reclaimed wool. Usually combined with new long fibers. Must be distinguished from virgin wool in labeling. See Legislation, Wool Products Labeling Act.

Resiliency. Property common to wool and silk causing them to spring back when crushed in the hand. Knit fabrics crease less easily than woven ones from similar yarns.

Resin finishes. Made in a variety of products. Chief uses are for water repellency and crisp finishes.

Resist print. Same principle as batik. See Batik.

Resloom®. Group of resins used to put finishes on cottons, wools, and blends with synthetics. They bestow a variety of properties; crease resistance, washability, improved texture.

Reused wool. Those wool fibers previously made into cloth and used by the consumer. They are inferior to reprocessed. See Legislation, Wool Products Labeling Act.

Reverse knit. Flat or plain knit used inside out to make a dull texture, as in wool or rayon jersey.

Fig. 47. Rib knit 1-1 cotton.

Reymet®. Aluminum yarn; staple and continuous filament with Mylar®, polyester. See Metallic cloth.

Rhovyl® vinyon. Manufactured in France. Used in bulk yarns, pile fabrics, and for industrial work clothes.

Rib. Variation of plain weave; having a vertical or horizontal cord of heavier yarns, usually in the filling, as in poplin. See Rib knit.

Rib knit. More elastic and durable than plain knit. Lengthwise ribs formed by single wales alternating on right and wrong sides. Called 1-1 rib. Fig. 47. Two wales alternating called 2-2 rib (also called Swiss rib). Fig. 48. 6-3 rib is common in men's hose.

Ribbon. Fig. 49.

(a) Narrow fabric, made in different widths of satin, grosgrain, taffeta, or velvet in silk, rayon, or nylon.

(b) Fused selvage of acetate rayon woven wide and cut with hot blades to seal edges. Velvet with acetate back makes velvet ribbon. Costs less and not as durable as woven selvage.

(c) Lacy bands of acetate rayon, treated for water repellency. Uses: florists' trade, gift wrapping. Lacelon®.

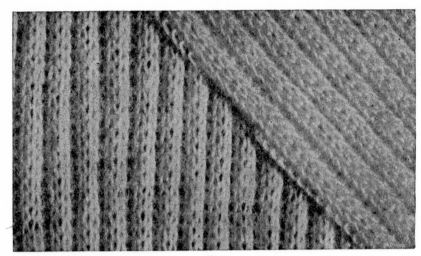

Fig. 48. Rib knit 2-2 cotton.

(d) Nonwoven or fused back. Vinyl plastic back, face of nylon filaments. Looks like satin. Sasheen®.

(e) Pile or velvet effect. Short fibers joined to fabric back by electrolytic process. See Flocked fabrics.

(f) Nonwoven crimped tie ribbon. Narrow tape for tying parcels.

(g) Cotton fibers treated similarly, dull surface, narrow, tough pliable paper, fluted.

Rigmel®. Shrinkage process used largely on cotton fabrics. Residual shrinkage may not be over 1 per cent.

Ripplette®. Cotton bedspread with alternating plain and ripple stripes; chiefly for hospital use. See Seersucker.

Roller printing. Power method of printing, more uniform and faster than early block printing or modern screen printing.

Romaine. Originally, a silk crepe; later a combination of yarns, rayon and acetate in both directions; having a plain weave, often called heavy sheer.

Rovana® saran micro-tape. Monofilament in form of folded tape; gives unique cross-section; width of tape varies with denier. In fabric form can be embossed, heat molded and

Fig. 49. Ribbons. Left to right: (1) Silk, woven selvage; (2) Acetate, fused edge; (3) Sasheen® nonwoven; nylon filaments fused to vinyl back.

sealed. Stable, flameproof; resists chemicals, mildew, solvents. Uses: home furnishings, especially casement curtains; industrial and automotive. See Fig. 50.

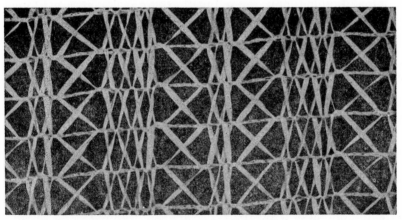

Fig. 50. Rovana® saran in Raschel knit construction for use as a flameproof casement fabric. "Interplay," original by Larsen Design Corporation.

Roving. Strand of fibers with less twist than yarn. Cotton roving is used in hand weaving, and to make cushion dots.

Rubber. Manufactured fiber. See Legislation.

Rubber sheeting. Plain cotton fabric with cured rubber on one side, may be napped. Largely replaced by plastic coated fabric.

Rug or Carpet. The following are the classes of floor coverings:

American Oriental	Frisé or Friese
Axminster	Velvet
Chenille	Wilton

See Oriental rugs.

Rug pad. To deaden sound, increase wear of rugs and prevent slipping of small rugs.
Sponge rubber of narrow thickness, cut to size. Jute and coarse hair, pressed into waffle pattern on one side, may have latex back.

Run resist. Knitting process which reduces number of runs in hosiery and underwear, especially those of rayon or nylon.

Run-of-the-mill. Merchandise as it comes from the mill, not inspected or finished.

Rush squares. Native grass or rush of natural color, from Indo-China, braided and sewn together, to make about 12-inch squares. These squares are joined to make any size desired. Made also of hemp or sisal.

S Twist. Direction of twist in yarn or cord, corresponding to the letter S. S and Z twist, Fig. 51. See Torque.

Sailcloth or duck. Heavy, plain weave cotton; having ply yarns which vary. May be white or in colors; striped or printed. Made also for sportswear, curtains, and upholstery. Usually a 2-1 variation of basket weave. See Fig. 79.

Sanforized®. A coined word, applied to woven fabrics, and products made therefrom, which have been mechanically treated and tested by the trade-mark proprietor so as to substantially eliminate subsequent shrinkage. Use of name licensed.

Fig. 51. S and Z twist yarn.

Sanforized Plus®. Trade mark applied to woven fabrics whose wash and wear property has been tested for smoothness after washing, for crease recovery, for shrinkage (see Sanforized®), for tensile strength, and for tear strength. Tested at mill level. Use of name licensed.

Sanitized®. Treatment of cotton goods for bacteria, fungus and odor retardance. Applied to canvas shoes, shoe lining, mattress covers, sheets.
See Odor resistant.

Saran. Generic term. See Legislation.

Saranspun® saran. Yarns used in various weaves for flameproof fabrics, especially casement curtains.

Sari (sah-ree). Handwoven silk garment for women of India; 5 yards or more long, 42-45″ wide. Made in pastel colors with stripes and woven border; sometimes with a surface pattern brocaded in silk or pure silver or gold; also made of cotton and synthetics. Modern sheer silk fabrics with metallic stripes are inspired by the original sari.

Sasheen®. Nonwoven nylon filaments fused to vinyl back. Looks like satin. See Ribbon.

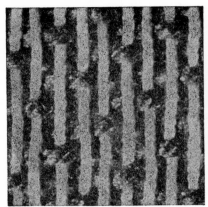 

Fig. 52. Satin weave. Warp face.   Fig. 53. Satin weave. Filling face.

Sateen. Satin weave in mercerized cotton usually of filling face; but better grades of warp face satin; plain or printed; dress goods, drapery uses. See Glosheen®.

Satin. See Weaves, satin.

   (a) Fabric of satin weave in cotton, all silk, rayon, nylon, or combination of any fibers with a cotton back. Designated as silk satin, rayon satin, or cotton satin. See Crepe back satin.

   (b) Lining satin is usually lighter in weight than dress satin. Often treated to resist perspiration.

   (c) Slipper satin. Heavy lustrous satin usually of rayon or acetate for slippers and wedding gowns.

   (d) Wash satin. Constructed for washability, of silk, rayon, or nylon; used in blouses and lingerie.

   (c) Upholstery satin. Usually has a cotton back, is heavier than dress satin. Satin weave. See Weaves.

   Warp-face Fig. 52.

   Filling-face Fig. 53.

Saylerized. Generic term for durable crisp finish on cotton goods, such as organdy. Fabric remains crisp after washing.

Schappe (shap). Another name for spun silk made from noil waste. Used in such novelty yarns as slub or knot.

Schiffli. Embroidery process by machine of same name.

Schreinerized (shrine-er-ized). Kind of calendering with diagonal embossed lines which produces high luster on sateen or cotton damask. Not durable through washing.

Scotch®. See Tapes.

Scotch® dusting fabric. Nonwoven or bonded fabric which picks up dust and holds it. Washable.

Scotchgard®. A stain repeller which can be applied to any fabric, making it repellent to water-borne and oil-borne stains. Used for rainwear, upholstery, clothing. May be washed or dry cleaned.

Scotchlite®. Reflective fabric used as trim; sewed on caps, gloves and outer garments. Fabric coated with very fine glass beads to reflect automobile lights at night. Fabric comes in different colors, and the reflective quality is durable after dry cleaning and washing.

Scott Apparel Foam®. See Laminated.

Scouring. Process of freeing wool from natural grease and foreign substances.

Screen print, or stencil method. Background of a design painted on a screen of bolting cloth or acetate fabric with paste; a separate screen being used for each color; dye is then printed through the exposed silk. Valued chiefly for a small printing order or an exclusive design.

Scrim. Lightweight, plain weave cotton fabric for window curtains. Marquisette is similar, but it has leno weave.

Scroop. Treatment of silk to give added body and characteristic rustle.

Sculptured. Term used to describe a raised or depressed effect produced by various methods, for example: a handwoven rug, having cut and/or uncut loops.

Also refers to hand-carved chenille rugs of thick pile, cut in grooves, after weaving, to outline the design.

See Chinese rug. See Velvet sculptured.

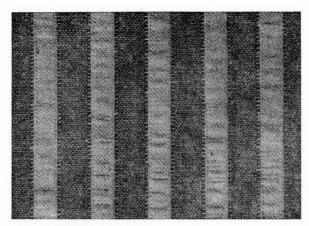

Fig. 54. Seersucker. Cotton.

Sea Island cotton. Grown on islands off the southern coast of the United States, also British West Indies. Fibers are fine, long, and lustrous; yarns used for sewing thread and a few high-grade fabrics.

Seamless. Hose knitted on a circular machine as distinguished from full fashioned. See Circular knit.

Seconds. Goods defective or below standard. Should be labeled "seconds," "irregular," or "imperfect."

Seersucker.
  (a) Cotton fabric known by alternating plain and puckered stripes achieved in weaving. Requires no ironing. Fig. 54. See Ripplette®.
  (b) Nylon. Puckered effect due to heat-setting of alternate groups of warp yarns.
  (c) Rayon or acetate similar to cotton fabric.

Selvage or selvedge. Old name was "list."
  (a) Finished warpwise edge on a woven or knitted fabric.
  (b) Tape selvage. Closely woven, usually wider and firmer than usual selvage. Seen in sheer cotton as voile and in sheeting.

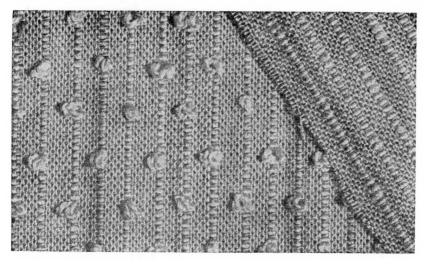

Fig. 55. Shagbark®. Cotton.

Serge. Fabric of even-sided 2-2 twill. Can be any fiber mixture or blend. See Twill.

(a) Cotton, rayon or other man-made fibers for linings; silk; see Surah.

(b) Worsted or in blends for women's wear 8–20 ozs., men's wear 14–24 ozs.

(c) French serge, fine and smooth, tends to wear shiny.

Sericin. Natural gum attached to silk filament. See Degumming. See Fibroin.

Shade cloth. Cotton fabric treated in various ways for window-shade cloth. Washability and flame resistance indicated on label. Fabric is usually coated with pyroxylin or a synthetic resin. Bontex®, Tontine®.

Shadow print. So-called shadow organdy is made by printing the fabric with insoluble white pigment. Also can be applied to rayon. See Pigment print.

Shagbark®. Cotton fabric, having an unusual surface texture due to fine loops in the warp yarns. Fig. 55. Made of combed cotton, it has fast color, a durable, crisp texture; is wash and wear, with a residual shrinkage of not more than 2 per cent.

Shaker. Heavy jersey for athletic sweaters, made of many 3-ply yarns.

Shantung. Originally silk from province of Shantung, China. See Pongee. Modern shantung is known by the slub yarns in shantung broadcloth whether of cotton, rayon or nylon. These are called "thick and thin" yarns.

Sharkskin. Women's worsted suiting of firm weave; made also of cotton; and of heavy dull acetate, although the latter has been largely replaced by Arnel® triacetate or blends. Usually carries a wash and wear label.

Sheer. Refers to thinness or transparency of any material.

Sheet wadding. Carded cotton in thin sheets with a glazed surface. See Quilting.

Sheeting.
   (a) Cotton, plain weave fabric made in two types: muslin and cambric. Sheeting is designated by width, 36″, 54″, 63″, 72″, 81″, 90″, by thread count, and weight in ozs. per sq. yd.
   (b) Linen sheeting is used for lunch cloths, napkins, uniforms.

Sheets. Made in standard widths and hemmed. Sold by types: 128, 140, 180, 200+, indicating sum of thread count, warp and filling. Count taken in gray goods. Some labels indicate count after washing. Sizes in inches:

   63 × 108   King size: 100 × 120
   72 × 108   108 × 122½
   81 × 108

Length is measured before hemming.
   (a) Percale sheets are finer and lighter in weight than muslin, and combed yarns superior to carded.
   (b) Colored sheets, also printed surface pattern.
   (c) Contour sheets, tailored to fit over end of mattress, especially valuable for crib sheets.

Shepherd's check. Name of any fabric with small even checks in white with black, brown, or blue; made of wool, cotton, rayon, nylon, or mixtures; and used for men's and women's clothing. May be of twill, plain, or basket weave.

Shetland wool. From sheep native to Scotland. Hand spun and knitted into delicate lacy shawls and sweaters, or made into a woven fabric such as Shetland tweed.

Shirley® cloth. Developed in England. Plain weave fabric, having 2 warps, 1 filling, made of combed cotton, 3-ply yarns of low twist, making a closely packed weave. Material is water repellent and wind resistant.

Shoddy.

(a) Derogatory term meaning inferior goods.

(b) Fibers recovered from previously woven or knitted material. See Reused wool.

Shrinkage.

(a) Raw wool loses weight because of the removal of grease in the scouring process.

(b) Refers to amount of contraction or relaxation any fabric undergoes in the finishing process or in subsequent washing. Release of tension on warp yarns, cotton or linen, which have been stretched and sized, causes them to shorten.

(c) Wool fabrics, woven or knitted, unless treated against shrinkage will contract and felt due to the combined effects of heat, moisture, and friction. Epidermal scales tend to interlock, and fibers to enmesh and fuse. See Fulling.

Shrinkage control. Treatment of yarn or fabric to reduce further shrinkage of finished goods.

(a) Cotton and other fabrics: Sanforized®, Rigmel®.

(b) Wool. See Chlorinated wool, Lanaset®, Resloom®, Dylanize®.

(c) For knit goods, Kroy®.

Sign cloth.

(a) Muslin, heavily sized, for printing.

(b) Silk or acetate, usually leno weave, resembles fine bolting cloth, for screen printing or to duplicate signs.

Silesia. Originally made in Silesia, a province of Prussia. Lightweight twill; calendered, cotton fabric used for suit linings. A heavy grade is used for trouser pockets.

Silk. Protein fiber, filament secreted by silkworms (*bombyx mori*) which feed on mulberry leaves. Raw silk (in the gum) is reeled directly from the cocoons. Waste silk is spun from pierced cocoons. See Wild silk. Sources of silk—Japan, Hong Kong, India.

Simtex®. Cotton table damask for institutional use, characterized by its durable linen-like finish.

Sisal (si-sal, see-sal).

(a) Fibers from a species of agave in Yucatan, used for hard fiber cordage, binder twine, and hammocks.

(b) Rugs woven of coarse twisted sisal fibers, without any spinning. Resembles Manila hemp. The rugs are reversible and made in a variety of weaves and widths for halls, offices, summer homes.

Sizing. Finishing process in which yarns or cloth are treated with a stiffening substance to give strength and smoothness.

Ski suiting. Heavy woolen fabric treated for water repellency. See Loden cloth.

Slicker fabric. Plain cotton cloth made water repellent by a coating of paraffin or other substance and used for fishermen's outfits and rainwear.

Slip cover fabric. Variety of weaves and textures, firmly woven of cotton, linen, rayon, and other synthetics. Sanforized® and treated for soil and water repellency.

Slippage. Due to loose weave or unevenly matched warp and filling, spaces may occur either in the warp way or filling way, usually in rayon, acetate, silk fabrics, or combinations.

Sliver (sly-ver). Continuous strand of loosely assembled fibers without twist.

Slub yarn.

(a) Soft, untwisted portion at intervals makes lumpy yarn for filling in various fabrics, such as slub broadcloth. See Yarns, Novelty.

(b) "Thick and thin" continuous filament rayon or nylon yarn, randomly spaced. Characterized by its simulated shantung silk effect.

Solution dyed. Synthetic fibers, dyed by the addition of colored pigments to the spinning solution. Trade names as Chromspun®, Jetspun®, Coloray®, Celaperm®.

Spandex. Generic term for Lycra®, a stretch yarn. See Legislation.

Spinneret.

(a) Small orifice in head of silkworm through which fibroin and sericin are secreted.

(b) Apparatus for producing filaments of manufactured fibers; a sort of fine sieve. The holes vary in diameter.

Spinning.

(a) Process of twisting fibers together to produce yarn or thread.

(b) Spinning of rayon, refers to the extrusion of spinning solution through spinneret.

Splicing. Reinforcement by extra yarn of cotton or nylon in heel, toe, or sole of hose for added strength.

Sponging. Shrinking of new wool goods before tailoring. May be labeled preshrunk from the mill. See London shrunk.

Spun-lo® viscose. Filament yarns for knit wear.

Spun rayon. See Staple.

Spun silk. Tangled or broken silk, which cannot be reeled from cocoons as filaments, is carded and spun for knitting and weaving. See Schappe. See Doupione.

Square weave. Plain-woven fabric with equal number of warp and filling yarns, e.g. 80-square percale.

Staple.
(a) Refers to length of textile fibers as long-staple wool.
(b) Staple cotton distinguished from linters.
(c) Refers to cut filaments of rayon or other synthetics to make spun yarns.
(d) Any standard fabric. Not a novelty.

Stazenu®. Durable finish on cotton for crease and soil resistance. Licensed use of trade mark.

Stock dyeing. See Dyeing.

Strand. Component part of yarn, as single, not plied.

Stretch yarns. Thermoplastics such as nylon or polyesters treated to produce elastic property in knit goods. Examples: Ban-Lon®, Helanca®. See Textralized®.
See Elastic yarn. High grade worsted for ski pants uses stretch nylon yarns.

Strié (stree-ay). Indistinct color stripes, warpwise. See Jaspé.

Stripping. Chemical process of destroying color in dyed cloth.

Structural fiber. Also called hard or leaf fiber, is made from the fleshy leaves of pineapple and abaca plants. The fiber is not spun, but tied end to end and used as yarn. See Piña.

Suede cloth (sway-d).
(a) Woven or knitted of cotton, rayon, wool, or nylon, finished by napping to resemble chamois leather. Used for gloves, linings, sport coats.
(b) Cotton twill with dense nap used for windbreakers.

Suiting. General term for large class of woolens, worsteds, and various blends in different weaves for men's and women's wear. See Tropical suiting.

Sunbak®. Double-faced cloth with high-count rayon satin interwoven with a wool, rayon, Acrilan®, or Dynel® blend which is napped for greater warmth. The one fabric serves as both lining and interlining.

Sundour®. Vat-dyeing process perfected by Morton Sundour in England. Guaranteed colorfast to sunlight and washing. Off the market for some years; now available.

Super Siri®. Underlining, interfacing, of 100 per cent spun viscose, available in different weights. Guaranteed shrinkage not in excess of 1 per cent. Automatically wash and wear. First known as Siri®.

SuPima®. Fine, silky, long staple cotton grown in the southwest United States. Yarns are used for dress goods, shirtings, laces, embroideries.

Suracel® acetate. Linings of fine twill, gas-fade-proof, perspiration-proof.

Surah.
(a) Originally silk in twill weave; now may be rayon, acetate, nylon or any synthetic. Plain, plaid, or printed for linings, kerchiefs, dresses.
(b) Heavy quality referred to as silk serge.

Swatch. Piece of cloth used as a sample, small or one yard or longer in length.

Swiss. So-called because first made in Switzerland.
(a) Fine, sheer, plain-woven cotton fabric; may be plain, or printed with dots or figures, or have woven, embroidered, or flock dots. Fabric is crisp or stiff, with no luster.
(b) Imported material with hand-tied dots, made on swivel loom.
Uses: dresses, aprons, curtains.

Swivel (swiv-el). Fabric having a woven figure which resembles embroidery, such as dotted Swiss, where individual shuttles make dots during the weaving. The ends of the yarn are tied by hand. See Swiss.

Syl-Mer®. Silicone finish for apparel, decorative fabrics, and leather to make them resist water and water-borne stains. Licensed use of trade mark.

Synthetic filaments. Fibers not found in nature but synthesized or built up from simpler substances as creations of the chemist: nylon, Orlon®, Dacron®, etc. Man-made is preferred to synthetic because many of the new fibers and finishes are not synthetic.

Synthetic resins. Used for finishing cotton and rayon fabrics to provide crease resistance, permanent pleats, or wash and wear qualities. New, improved products constantly appearing.

Tabby. Another name for plain weave, as in voile, muslin.

Tablecloth. Variety of fabrics used for table covers in linen, cotton, rayon, nylon, and combinations; in plain weave as Indian head®, woven stripe, block pattern, or damask; also lace fabrics. Sold as yardage or finished table coverings or cloths in standard sizes. See Damask. See Simtex®.

Table padding.

   (a) Cotton fabric, plain or twill, with thick nap on both sides. May be loosely woven with soft roving for filling.

   (b) Quilted goods of plain weave, similar to mattress pad.

   (c) Any of above also used for ironing board pads.

Tackle twill®. Twill weave rayon with 3-ply combed cotton filling; characterized by unusual tensile strength. Used for sportswear, uniforms, rainwear.

Taffeta.

   (a) Originally stiff, plain weave silk; piece-dyed, or yarn-dyed of stripes or plaid; also print and warp print. Made in many varieties such as tissue taffeta, which is soft and lightweight; and paper taffeta, which has a stiff finish.

   (b) Taffeta of rayon, acetate, nylon, or combinations has the same uses as does silk: for dresses, suits, and draperies.

   (c) So-called cotton taffeta is used for slip covers, often combined with rayon.

Tapes—various widths and uses.

   (a) Adhesive. Cellophane type Scotch®, Texcel®. Plastic adhesive type Curad®.

Fig. 56. Tapestry. Handwoven wool.

(b) Mending. Heat sealing. Cotton fabric coated with cellulose acetate. With application of a hot iron the tape fuses to worn spots and makes laminated fabrics. Bondex®, Permacel®.

(c) Pressure sensitive. Widely used in industry; may have cloth or plastic surface; 36″ or narrow for tapes. Permacel®, Scotch®, Texcel®.

(d) Woven. Various narrow widths of plain twill or herringbone weave in cotton, linen, nylon, or rayon, to be used for tying.

Tapestry. Originally handwoven pictorial hanging or furniture covering, such as the Gobelins in Paris. Used to limited extent in modern homes and clubs. Machine reproductions are clever imitations done on a Jacquard loom in combinations of various yarns. Fig. 56, handwoven, Fig. 57, machine reproduction.

Fig. 57. Tapestry. Machine reproduction.

Tarlatan. Thin, open, plain-woven cotton; highly-sized, comes in white and colors; will not launder, fades in sun. May have a flame-resistant finish. Used for pageant costumes, Christmas stockings, and for bed canopies instead of mosquito netting.

Tarpoon®. Closely woven cotton, of 2-ply yarn, gingham type; water repellent, shrinkage controlled, crease resistant. Uses: jackets, play wear. 45″ wide.

Tartan. Scotch worsted plaids in traditional patterns and colors for the various clans, such as Campbell, MacPherson, and Stewart. Fig. 58. Made in Scotland, or domestic copy.

Taslan®. Inter-textured yarn; a special process for making bulky lightweight Dacron® or nylon, or other fibers. Yarns may be decorative as well as suitable for knitted or woven fabrics. Material is resistant to abrasion or pilling.

Tattersall.

(a) Simple check pattern usually in two colors on white; for vests and sport shirts. Fig. 59.

(b) A casual vest, named for Lord Tattersall.

Teasel. Prickly burr used for raising nap on fine woolens.

Fig. 58. Tartan. Stewart clan. Prince Charles Edward Stewart ("Bonnie Prince Charlie").

Tebilized®. Applies only to fabrics regularly tested by owners of this trade mark, and which conform to specified standards of crease resistance and quality established by them.

Tempra® viscose. High tenacity yarns.

Tentering. Finishing process for stretching cloth to desired width. Small holes on selvage of wool flannel show the marks of tenterhooks.

Terylene®. British polyester filament and staple fiber. The fabric has strength and wrinkle resistant properties and is used in men's suits and sportswear.

Terry. Cotton fabric with loops on both sides. See Turkish towels. Yardage is made into bathrobes, beach wear, slippers, and draperies. May be yarn-dyed or fabric-printed and is reversible.

Texcel®. See Tapes.

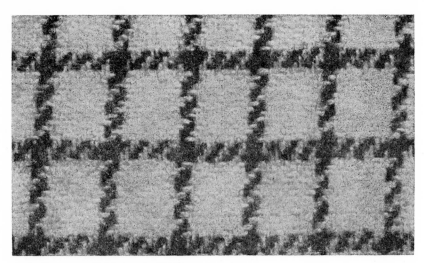

Fig. 59. Tattersall (magnified).

Textralized®. Crimped type of continuous synthetic fibers used to make bulky yarns for sweaters and lingerie. See Ban-Lon®. Licensed use of trade mark.

Texture. Appearance and touch of fabric described as lustrous, dull, stiff, soft, heavy, sheer, woolly, etc., due to kind of yarn, weave, or finish. The texture of a carpet depends on whether it has cut or uncut pile, or high and low pile.

Textured yarns.

(a) May be made of filament nylon or other thermoplastic fibers for various end uses. Example: Caprolan®, for carpet yarns.

(b) Used in place of spun yarns, eliminates problem of pilling.

(c) May be curled, coiled, crimped, or looped.

For diagrams of these techniques see American Fabrics No. 46, Spring 1959. See References.

Thai (tie) silk. First made for Siamese royalty. Handwoven of pure silk in Thailand homes for export trade. Characterized by rich oriental colors and plain weave. May be of self color, stripes, or plaids. The warp and filling in different colors gives an iridescent effect. Metal yarns are sometimes introduced.

Theatrical gauze. Linen of plain open weave resembling scrim. Used for background of stage scenery and for window curtains.

Thermoplastic. The property some fibers have of becoming plastic under heat. Fabrics retain durable pleats. Examples: acetate, nylon, polyesters, acrylics. See Heat sealing.

Thermosetting. See Heat setting.

Thread. Distinguished from yarn used in weaving and knitting.
  (a) Sewing cotton is usually six-cord (3-ply) thread, each ply double and mercerized or glazed.
  (b) Linen, silk, and nylon are made into sewing thread, also darning cotton or silk. See Nymo®.

Thread count. See Tests.

Thrums. Ends of warp unwoven, remaining in the loom.

Ticking. Closely woven cotton fabric, usually featherproof, used for pillows and mattresses.
  (a) Heavy blue and white striped twill is called ACA ticking. Sold by weight as 8 or 9 ounces. For hospital use it is plastic coated.
  (b) Printed sateen type, tough, and firm, is used for mattresses and pillows.
  (c) Damask. Jacquard woven design, often in two colors, mercerized or combined with rayon, for mattress covers.
  (d) Bohemian. Fine, close, plain weave, stripe of white with colored filling.
  (e) Lightweight ticking is used for women's wear.

Tie dye. Hand method of producing patterns on cloth by tying portions with string or gathering on a thread. The tied areas resist the dye and thus make the design. Native to India and Japan; may be imitated in machine printing.

Tire fabric. Cotton of many-ply hard twist yarns. Now replaced by high tenacity rayon or nylon.

Fig. 60. Toile de Jouy.

Tissue gingham. See Gingham.

Toile de Jouy (Fr. "Cloth of Jouy"; pr. twal-de-zhoo-y). A pictorial monochromatic print on white or light cotton which originated in France during the 18th or 19th centuries; reproduced in rayon. American designs use same idea; also for wallpaper. Fig. 60.

Tontine®. Cotton fabric, pyroxylin treated on both sides, used for window shades and stage curtains. Material is waterproof, washable, flame resistant.

Top. Long parallel wool fibers left after the noils have been removed by combing.

Topel® (toe-pel). Cross-linked rayon. See Corval®. Fabrics may contain 100 per cent Topel® or be softer textured blends containing cotton, acetate, or nylon. Dyeing similar to cotton.

Topping. One color dyed on top of another, as yellow dipped in red to produce red-orange; or black and white checks or plaids in wool later dyed a color over the white.

Torque (Fr., "twisted"; pr. tork). Term used to describe S and Z twist as right hand torque or left hand torque. Technically the term refers to the characteristic of stretch yarn that tends to make it turn on itself as a result of twisting.

Non-torque yarns. Stretch yarns which have no tendency to rotate when they are permitted to hang freely.

Tow (toe).

(a) Short flax fiber in contrast to line, long fibers.

(b) Term applied to a long, ropelike bundle of man-made filaments not yet cut or broken into staple.

Toweling.

(a) Narrow yard goods in the following: Bird's-eye weave, crash, damask, glass towel, honeycomb, huck, twill, terry; cotton, linen, or blends with rayon.

(b) Hemmed towels are often woven with borders. Hotels and hospitals have their names woven in white or color.

Tracing cloth. Plain-woven cotton fabric, made of fine combed yarn, treated for transparency and water repellency. Used by architects and engineers.

Trade names. Indicated by ® registered trade mark. May refer to man-made fibers as Acrilan®, Dacron®, Dynel®, Orlon®. Also may be applied to fabrics or finishes used exclusively by a manufacturer to designate his product.

Triacetate. Related to acetate. May be used as generic term.

Tricot (tree-ko). Type of warp knit structure having vertical wales on the right side and horizontal wales on the wrong side. It is a kind of jersey. Fig. 61.

(a) Nylon tricot is produced in different weights; chiffon or tissue tricot is very sheer and used for lingerie.

(b) Firm fabric of same construction in cotton, nylon, or Dacron®, used for gloves and brassieres.

Tricotine. Steep twill, warp face worsted with double line suggesting knit structure. See Elastique. See Cavalry twill.

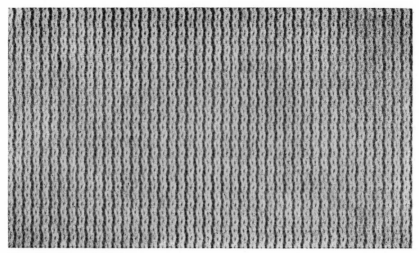

Fig. 61. Tricot. Nylon.

Trilok®. Three-dimensional fabric with puffed surface and lateral porosity. Woven of shrinkable plastic yarn with natural or synthetic yarns. Used in industry.

Tropical type suiting. Not to be confused with tropical worsted. Lightweight suiting for men's wear usually made from blends or mixtures of cotton or wool with any of the man-made fibers.

Tropical worsted. Lightweight worsted suiting of fine yarns made in a variety of weaves; used for men's summer suits, women's suits. Suitings of this type come in various weaves and textures, blending or combining different fibers or yarns.

Tubular fabric.

(a) Plain weave cotton or linen with no seam, as for pillow cases.

(b) Many braids are tubular.

(c) Tubular knit fabric used for men's neckties.

(d) Jersey and many other knit fabrics are made on a circular knitting frame.

Tufted carpets. These are made on a pre-woven backing mesh, usually jute or cotton. Pile yarns are then tufted into this fabric,

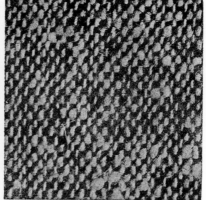

Fig. 62. Tweed. Hound's tooth.   Fig. 63. Tweed. Donegal.

and the tufts firmly locked by a backing of latex compound. Widths up to 18' wide.

Tulle (tool). Mesh finer than other nets made of silk or nylon and used for wedding veils, formals.

Turkey red. Fast red dye on cotton, made from vegetable madder or modern synthetic madder. Plain red calico dyed thus is called Turkey red. Madder dye was originally brought from Turkey.

Tweed. Made originally in Scotland from coarse, hand spun wool yarn woven on hand looms. May be plain, twill, or herringbone weave, or have district checks such as hound's tooth, Fig. 62, or gun club. Scottish: clan tartans; Irish: Donegal, Fig. 63, and Connemara. Texture of tweed is often simulated in cotton, silk and blends.

Twill weave. Fundamental type in which the intersections of the yarns form diagonal lines across the fabric. Commonest twill is 2-2 as in serge; Fig. 64. The direction of the twill is from lower left hand to upper right hand. 1-3 Fig. 65, 4-1 Fig. 66, Herringbone, Fig. 67.

Tycora®. Refers to all processed continuous filament yarns and combinations made by one company. A smooth type is pro-

Fig. 64. Twill 2-2. Even sided.   Fig. 65. Twill 1-3. Filling face.
Reconstruction.   Reconstruction.

duced for shirts; bouclé yarn for sweaters; and processed yarns
for carpets.

Tyrex® viscose. Rayon tire cord of high tenacity; not thermoplastic as is the nylon product.

Tyron® rayon. Tire cord or tire fabric. See High tenacity rayon.

Unfinished worsted. Worsted with a slight nap which obscures
the weave. Worsted typically has little finish.

Uniform cloths. For military services, policemen, guards, etc.
Serge, melton, elastique are commonly used; raincoats are of
cotton, nylon, or rayon. Colors distinctive for Army, Navy and
Air Force. Olive drab or khaki in cotton is used for summer
uniforms.

Union. Fabrics of cotton warp and linen filling, as huck towel,
called union huck; or cotton warp and wool filling.

Upland cotton. Short staple grown in southern states; distinguished from long staple, as Egyptian and Pima.

V-shaped pile. A closely woven pile, as Lyons-type velvet, used
for collars and for lightweight corduroys. Fig. 68. Fig. 69.
See W-shaped pile.

Fig. 66. Twill 4-1.   Fig. 67. Twill. Herringbone.

Vat-dye. Dyes developed by oxidation, originally made in vats, as indigo. Vat-dye label insures superior dye. May be yarn-dyed or printed.

Vegetable fibers. See Natural fibers.

(a) Bast or soft fibers; from inner bark of flax, hemp, jute, or ramie.

(b) Hard or leaf; from leaf stems of abaca, henequen, pine-apple or sisal.

(c) Seed hairs from boll or fruit of cotton plant.

Velcro®. Nylon closure to replace slide fasteners. Two strips of woven nylon material are used. One surface of one strip is covered with tiny filament hooks; the other strip is of a felt-like nylon material with tiny nylon loops on one surface. These two fabrics placed together become fastened, but can be pulled apart. The tape is ½" to 2" wide in white, black, and colors. Used on slip covers, sports jackets, belt closings. Talon Zephyr® is another type of nonmetal closing.

Velon® (vee-lon) saran. Vinyl chloride film and sheeting used for clothing, housewares, swimming pools and/or embossed

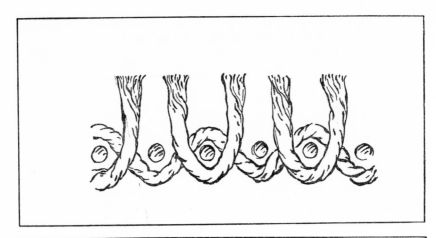

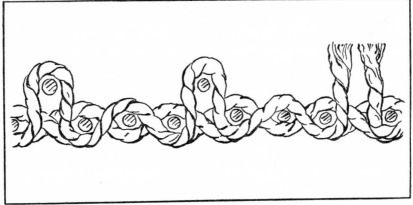

Fig. 68. (Upper) V-shaped pile. Cross-section. Cut loops. Fig. 69. (Lower) W-shaped pile. Cross-section. Cut and uncut loops.

washable upholstery. In monofilament form is woven into fabrics for luggage, upholstery, etc.

Velour (Fr., "velvet"; pr. ve-loor). General term for pile fabrics.

(a) Wool velour, napped coating.

(b) Hat felt called velour made from fur fibers, napped.

Velvet. Broad and inclusive term which covers all warp pile fabrics except plush and terry. Velvet requires two warps, two sets of filling yarns and a fifth to make the pile. Two fabrics are woven double, face to face, and cut apart, while still on the loom, by a thin knife which moves back and forth like a shuttle. Fig. 38.

(a) V-shaped pile used for close or heavyweight fabrics, and W-shaped pile for lightweight fabrics.

(b) Chiffon velvet is lightweight, drapable, of rayon or nylon.

(c) Costume velvet is wide velveteen, with a thick pile, highly mercerized.

(d) Lyon's type velvet: characterized by erect pile of silk, rayon, or nylon, used for millinery and trimmings such as collars.

(e) Nylon: very resilient, less lustrous than rayon.

(f) Panne (pan): lightweight velvet with pile laid flat in one direction.

(g) Sculptured velvet has an acetate pile, rayon back. Embossed with hot metal roll which makes a smooth, shiny background of design, while the pile stands in relief.

Velvet carpet. Machine made; mostly of solid colors, has the appearance of velvet with a cut pile, uses yarns of woolen or high quality worsted.

Velveteen. Filling-faced pile fabrics, originally called fustian. Woven with soft mercerized filling yarns which form floats, lat to be cut and brushed into short pile. Back may be plain o. ill weave; material has a wide variety of uses.

Ven n. Warp-faced heavy sateen; tightly woven; used for g nt linings. Also made of rayon.

Ver (vu-rel) modacrylic. Fiber made into yarns having a so uxurious hand; resilient, lightweight, pleat retentive, res nt to pilling, and to flame; and immune to moths and mil . Used in pile fabrics.

Vicuñ (vee-koon-ya). Small wild animal of the camel family native to the high Andes. Their extremely fine and soft fur is spun and woven in exclusive coatings.

Vigoureux (vee-goor-uh). Named for the inventor, this is a process of printing worsted fibers before spinning, to give a mixed color effect.

Vinal. Generic term. See Legislation.

Vinyl products.

(a) Nonwoven, water repellent, flame resistent material used for furniture upholstery, wall covering, headboards, folding doors. Velon®, Naugahyde®, Koroseal®.

(b) Sheet vinyl. Embossed or printed, may be laminated to fabric backing.

Vinyon. Generic term. See Legislation.

Virgin wool. Wool not previously manufactured into cloth. Term also applied to nylon, as virgin nylon.

Visca®. Artificial straw or imitation of hair for hat braid, made from monofilament rayon.

Viscose rayon. One of the processes by which rayon is manufactured. Made chiefly from wood pulp.

Viyella® (vye-yella) flannel. Originated in England, consisting of 55 per cent merino lamb's wool and 45 per cent long staple Egyptian cotton.

(a) In twill weave comes in white and pastel for infants' wear. Also produced in solid colors, checks, plaids, and prints for shirts, dresses, and pajamas in various weights. Because it is a blend of cotton and wool, this fabric is shrink resistant. 36″ wide.

(b) Viyella® socks are made from Viyella® yarns spun in England; permanently mothproof, nonshrinking.

Voile. Thin, transparent fabric in plain weave. See Ninon.

(a) Cotton: best quality of 2-ply combed yarns with hard twist. Inferior quality, single yarns tend to become fuzzy. May be plain or printed. Uses: dresses, blouses, lingerie, curtains.

(b) Nylon: very transparent for lingerie or trimmings.

(c) Silk: fine sheer fabric. Dresses, nuns' veils.

(d) Wool: thin smooth and wiry worsted yarns tightly twisted for dresses.

Vycron® polyester. Filament staple and tow for blends and combinations with cotton, Bemberg®, viscose rayon, wool, etc. End uses for fabrics include apparel, home furnishings and industrial. Resists pilling, is wrinkle resistant, not affected by acids or alkalies. Also Vycron® fiber-fill.

Vyrene® spandex. Extruded monofilament of the spandex family used as core for wraps of textile yarns.

W-shaped pile. Used in rayon velvet and some grades of corduroy where pile ends are less closely anchored than in V-shaped pile. See Velvet. See V-shaped pile.

Wale. Refers to the width of the cords in corduroy. Also to rows of loops or stitches, lengthwise, in knit goods.

Warp. The set of yarns running lengthwise in a piece of cloth. See End.

Warp-knit fabric. Made by intricate mechanism of flat knitting machine. Fabric is closer, less elastic than weft knits or jersey; may be made from yarns of any fiber or combinations, used for gloves, lingerie and novelty knits. See Tricot, Milanese.

Warp print. Process of printing design on warp before weaving; gives shadowy design. Used on silk, cotton, rayon, etc. for taffeta or satin material. Imitated in direct print.

Wash and wear. Fabrics which may be washed and worn without ironing because of shrink and wrinkle resistant finish. See Drip dry.

Waterproofing. Method of impregnating or coating fabric, usually with oil, rubber, lacquer, resin or vinyl; used to make rain apparel, awnings, etc. See Coated fabrics.

Water repellency. Various treatments to prevent penetration of water; which do not close the interstices or pores of a fabric as waterproofing does. Cravanette®, Zelan®, Norane®, Syl-mer®. See Tests—water repellency.

Weaves. Known by the manner of interlacing warp and filling.

   Fundamental types. Fig. 70.

     Plain—muslin or taffeta.

       Variations.

         Rib—poplin.

         Basket—monk's cloth.

     Twill:

       2-2 serge.

       2-1 drill.

       Variations:

       Herringbone, other varieties of twill.

     Satin:

       Warp face—satin fabric.

       Filling face—sateen.

   Figures:

       Small geometric pattern on dobby loom as bird's-eye, huck.

       Jacquard—brocade, damask, tapestry.

       Lappet—warpwise loom embroidery.

       Clipped dot or small figure.

   Pile:

       Uncut—see Terry—not a true pile.

       Warp pile—velvet.

       Filling pile—corduroy and velveteen.

   Miscellaneous:

       Leno—marquisette.

       Double weave.

       Combinations of the above types.

       Novelty weaves.

Web. Refers to partly woven cloth or warp in the loom.

Webbing. Strong, and closely woven narrow fabric; may be cotton, jute, linen, rayon, etc., for various uses, as upholstery webbing.

Weft. Same as woof or filling.

BLACK=WARP   WHITE=FILLING

Plain   Honeycomb

Twill 2-1   Twill 2-2

Satin, Warp   Bird's-Eye

Fig. 70. Weaves. Fundamental types.

Weight of wool goods. Women's wear as sheers, voile 6 ozs.; to 20 ozs. for suits; for men's wear, made in 14–24 ozs. per sq. yd.

Weighted silk. Term rarely used. Formerly silk was given added weight by the addition of metallic salts in the dyeing or finishing processes. For certain uses where no cleaning is involved.

Whipcord. Steep twill similar to gabardine; worsted, woolen, or heavy cotton, for riding habits, uniforms, and outdoor garments.

Wicking. Narrow, woven cotton fabric of coarse, soft-spun yarns; flat or tubular; used as wicks and packing in machinery.

Widths of cloth. Vary with uses. There is a tendency to weave wider cloths for advantage in cutting garments. In general: cottons are woven 36″–39″–45″ wide; drapery fabric wider; wools range 54″–60″ wide; some silk imports 36″ wide.

Wigan. Canvas-like cotton fabric, closer than crinoline, made in varying degrees of stiffness. Used by tailors for interlining fronts of men's coats.

Wild silk. Coarse, tan, or natural color filament produced by a species of silkworm which cannot be cultivated. Used to make pongee. Incorrectly called "raw silk."

Wilton rug. First made in Wilton, England. Characterized by a dense pile, cut loops; having cotton, or jute, or both for backing. Colors in pattern limited; controlled by Jacquard loom.

Woof. Same as weft or filling.

Wool. Natural fiber, originating as the covering of sheep. Characterized by a strong, resilient, bulking quality, high absorbency, ability to take dye, and resistance to soil. Its felting power is an advantage in making mechanical felt, but a disadvantage is the tendency of woolens to shrink in washing unless processed to prevent shrinkage. Wool is the least flammable of all textiles. Wool blankets are used to smother fires. Wool fiber, Fig. 71.

Wool bat. Carded wool or blended cotton and wool sold in laps for filling comforters. See Dacron® fiber-fill.

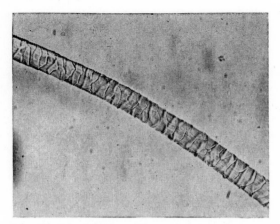

Fig. 71. Wool Fiber. Photomicrograph.

Woolen.

    (a) Yarns for knitting or weaving made from short fibers mixed loosely before spinning; tend to shrink more than worsted yarn.

    (b) Cloth made of woolen yarn may be fulled after weaving and finished by napping, as in wool broadcloth.

Worsted (woo-sted). Yarn made from relatively long wool fibers, laid parallel before spinning. See Top.

    (a) Smooth fabric as gabardine made from worsted yarns tightly twisted with a distinct weave; incorrectly called hard finish.

    (b) Some worsteds have a softer surface if the yarns are spun for this effect or if a slight finish is employed. See Unfinished worsted.

Woven labels. Name or insignia, Jacquard woven. Width: narrow to 12″.

Wrinkl-shed®. Resin finish for durable wrinkle and mildew resistance. Shrinkage control less than 2 per cent.

Yardage. Cloth sold by running yard to distinguish from finished garments, rugs, blankets, etc.

Fig. 72. Yarns, single and many-ply. Left to right: (1) single, (2) 2-ply, (3) 4-ply, (4) multiple strand, (5) cable or cord, three strands of multiple strands.

Yarn.

(a) Made by twisting together (spinning) fibers, natural, or man-made. Used for weaving or knitting. See Ply.

(b) Thrown silk or continuous filaments of synthetic fibers require no spinning, yet serve as yarns.

(c) Monofilament, as saran used as a yarn.

See Novelty yarns.

Yarns—single and many ply, Fig. 72.

See Coated, Creped, Durene®.

Yarn-dyed. Yarns dyed before weaving or knitting.

Yarn number. Relative measure of fineness; incorrectly called yarn count. Spun yarns based on standard lengths per standard weight for cotton, wool, linen, silk and man-made fibers. See Denier.

Yarn slippage. Displacement of yarns adjacent to stitched seam resulting in gap. Occurs usually in loosely woven rayon, acetate or silk fabrics or combination weaves.

Z twist. Direction of twist in yarn or cord which corresponds to letter Z. S and Z twist Fig. 51. See Torque.

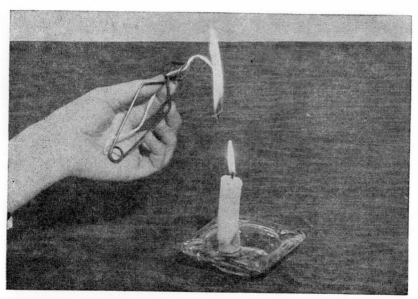

Fig. 73. Test. Burning cotton yarn in flame.

Zantrel® polynosic. Differs in molecular structure from conventional rayon. Has a low degree of water absorption, resists caustic solutions, has high wet strength, and high elastic recovery. Used in wash and wear fabrics, shirtings, and women's wear.

Zefran® (zeff-ran). Modified acrylic fiber. Staple form spun and bulk yarns, used alone or in blends. Fabrics washable, wrinkle resistant; for woven and knitted apparel.

Zelan®. Durable water-repellent finish primarily on cotton or viscose rayon fabrics; stain resistant. Allows air to circulate freely. Durable after washing and dry cleaning.

Zephyr. Implies light weight and airiness. Fine worsted yarn used for knitting and crocheting.

Zeset®. Durable wrinkle resistant finish primarily on cotton or viscose rayon fabrics. Zeset® and Zelan® may be applied to same fabric.

Fig. 74. Test. Burning wool yarn in flame.

Zibeline. Heavy woolen coating characterized by a long shaggy nap laid in one direction; also in lightweight fabric for suits.

Part II Tests—
Identification of Fibers
and Fabrics

"We are past the point of knowing by touch," said a department store buyer. Before the development of man-made fibers, the careful buyer judged by *feel*. A piece of wool was all wool; it felt warm, was springy or resilient; when crushed in the hand it would return to its original shape; it would not hold a crease. Linen was smooth, cool, heavier than cotton of the same construction; held creases unless treated for crease resistance. Silk was lustrous, and, if not weighted, was resistant to creases. Cotton did not know modern finishes. It was classed as the least valuable of the fibers.

Weight of comparable fabrics was judged superficially by lifting; for example, a blanket. All wool would be lighter than cotton and wool of same size and construction.

These old-fashioned ways of judging no longer hold good. Blends of many fibers and numerous finishes baffle the experts. Fortunately, labels and hang tags on yardage and garments give the fiber content and often rules for care of fabrics. See Textile Fiber Products Identification Act, p. 145.

PHYSICAL TESTS

Burning Identification.

The simplest of all tests is burning. It is the best quick, easy

Fig. 75. Test. Burning silk fabric.

method of identification for 100 per cent fibers, although not for blends.

A group of warp or filling yarns held by tweezers and applied to a match will show the following:

Cellulose fibers. Cotton, Fig. 73, linen, ramie, and jute burn with a flash like paper with the odor of burning paper; the soft ash is black or gray in color and not self-extinguishing. Afterglow occurs especially in fabrics of compact construction, such as cotton duck. Viscose rayon or regenerated cellulose burns much like cotton, leaves the same type of ash.

Protein fibers. Wool, hair, and natural fur burn slowly with the strong characteristic odor of burning feathers. They end in a bead or ball, easily crushed. When removed from flame, they will not support combustion. Fig. 74.

Pure silk burns in the same manner, with slight odor. **Fig. 75.**

Man-made fibers. Thermoplastic. Examples:

Fig. 76. Test. Burning acetate fabric.

Acetate rayon melts and burns; does not shrink away from flame. Residue is a hard, black, plastic bead. Fig. 76.

Nylon. 100 per cent nylon tricot shows edge fusing or melting. Nylon shrinks away from the flame. Residue is a plastic tan bead; returns to molten stage. Fig. 77.

Mineral fibers. Examples:

Fiberglas® becomes blackened but not burned. Changes form only at blast-furnace temperature.

Asbeston® resists burning, will not support a flame.

Thread Count.

Closeness of weave may be determined by use of pick glass or linen tester with inch scale. Figs. 78, 79. Warp yarns are counted in an inch space at five different places and the average taken. The same is done for the filling. Thread count is indicated

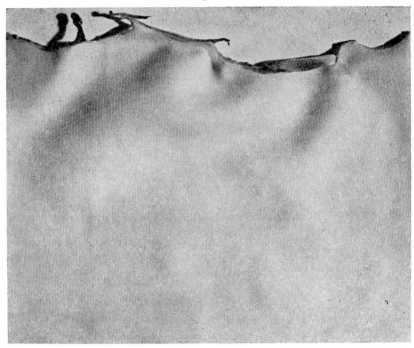

Fig. 77. Test. Burning nylon fabric.

Fig. 78. Linen tester. For thread count see Fig. 79.

Fig. 79. Sail cloth (magnified). Modified basket weave 1-2.

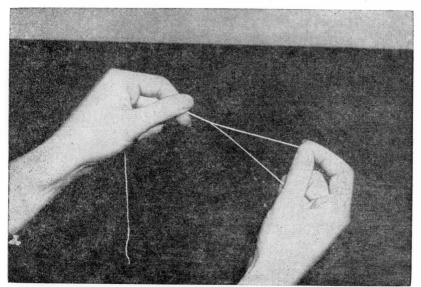

Fig. 80. Examination of yarn. Untwisting 2-ply yarn.

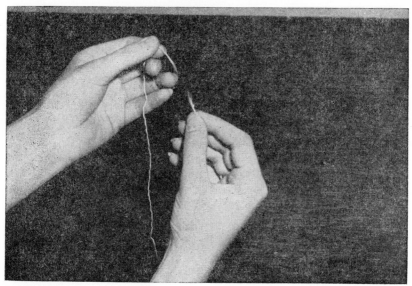

Fig. 81. Examination of fibers.

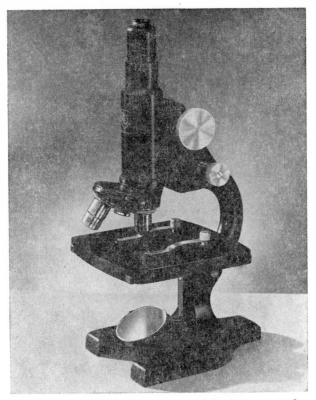

Fig. 82. Microscope. Student model. See Appendix, Testing equipment.

as 72 × 68 (±); the first number standing for the warp and the second for the filling. If the count is the same both ways it is indicated as square, e.g. 80 square percale. See Standards for Sheets, p. 149.

Examination of Yarns.

By raveling a few warp and filling yarns, one can observe their size, twist, and smoothness. The presence of two or more ply is shown when a yarn is untwisted as in Fig. 80. Sometimes the composition is evident from the appearance of bright or dull rayon, smooth worsted, or fuzzy woolen yarn. The character of a core yarn may often be determined by untwisting it; likewise,

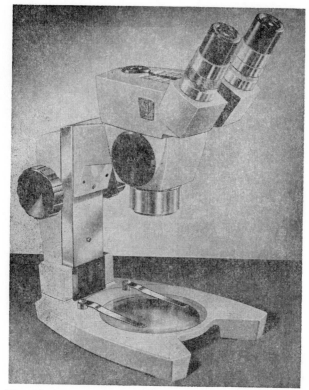

Fig. 83. Microscope. Cycloptic. See Appendix, Testing equipment.

novelty yarns show combinations of fibers and varying textures in the individual plies. Since yarns largely determine the character of the cloth, this test is important.

Examination of Fibers.

By untwisting a yarn, and breaking it gently, one can observe how the exposed fibers show their characteristics. Fig. 81. Wool and crimped synthetics appear kinky; filament rayon is straight; linen breaks with long tapering ends; while cotton has brushlike ends, except mercerized cotton which may resemble linen. Fibers are obtained from yarns in this way in order to make microscopic mounts.

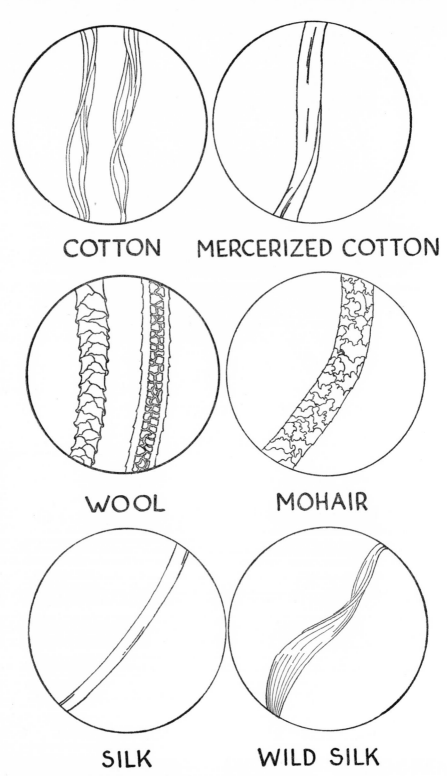

COTTON MERCERIZED COTTON

WOOL MOHAIR

SILK WILD SILK

Fig. 84. Fiber characteristics.

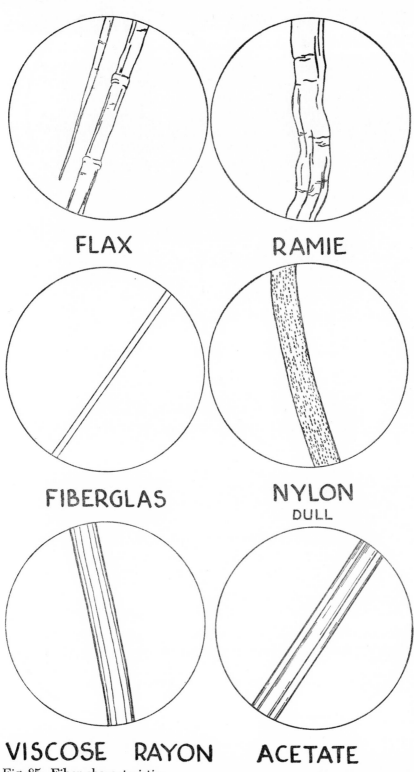

FLAX

RAMIE

FIBERGLAS

NYLON
DULL

VISCOSE RAYON

ACETATE

Fig. 85. Fiber characteristics.

Microanalysis.

This is slower than a chemical test but useful when two or more fibers occur in a blend. See Microscope, Figs. 82, 83. Identify the fibers by their characteristics. Figs. 84, 85. Photomicrographs of some man-made fibers, longitudinal and cross-section views (×500), are shown in Figs. 86-97.*

Color reactions have not been described. These tests require white samples.

CHEMICAL TESTS

Acetone test (for identification of acetate and Arnel® triacetate in mixture or blend with other fibers). Place sample on watch glass or dish, cover with acetone. Acetate fibers are dissolved in 80 per cent acetone; Arnel® triacetate fibers, in 100 per cent acetone. Combination acetate and rayon. Fig. 98.

Acid test (for identification of cellulosic fibers). Place sample on newspaper, to protect ironing board. Put a few drops of dilute sulfuric acid, 2-4 per cent solution, in middle of a sample, using hollow glass rod. Place paper over the sample, to protect iron; with a hot iron press on top of the paper. When sample has been dried remove and touch lightly with iron to finally dry it, but not scorch. Now rub sample vigorously, hold to the light. Example: Viyella® flannel, blend of cotton and wool; the cotton will be dusted out, leaving the wool. Fig. 99. In case of cotton warp, the wool filling will remain. If the cotton has not been weakened sufficiently, use second application of acid.

Alkali test (for identification of protein fibers).

Home method: Place sample of convenient size in enamel cup or pan; do not use aluminum. Cover with lye solution, using a rounded tablespoon of household lye to a pint of water; the strength varies with its freshness. Cover and boil 5-7 minutes. The wool or silk will be destroyed and residue will show cotton, rayon, linen or any synthetic present. Wash in dilute vinegar and

*Reprinted with permission of The American Society for Testing Materials (A.S.T.M.), Standards on Textile Materials Committee D-13, 1961.

Photomicrographs

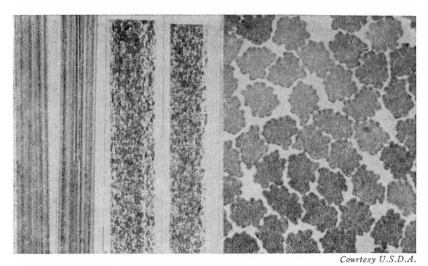

Fig. 86. Viscose rayon. (Left) Longitudinal. (Right) Cross-section.

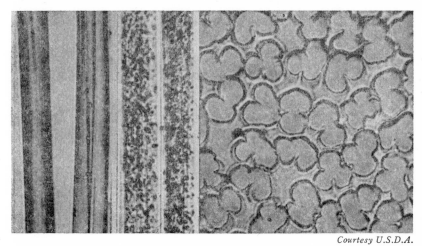

Fig. 87. Acetate. (Left) Longitudinal. (Right) Cross-section.

Photomicrographs

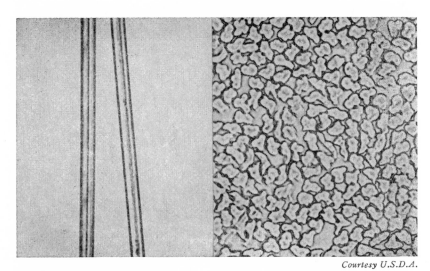

Fig. 88. Cuprammonium® rayon. (Left) Longitudinal. (Right) Cross-section.

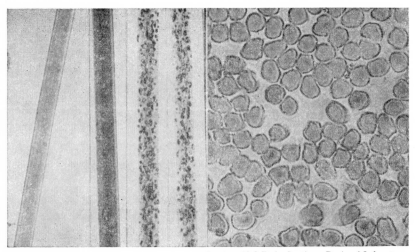

Fig. 89. Fortisan® rayon. (Left) Longitudinal. (Right) Cross-section.

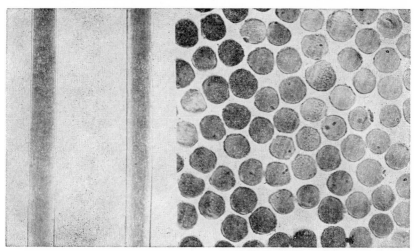

Fig. 90. Nylon 6-6. Regular. (Left) Longitudinal. (Right) Cross-section.

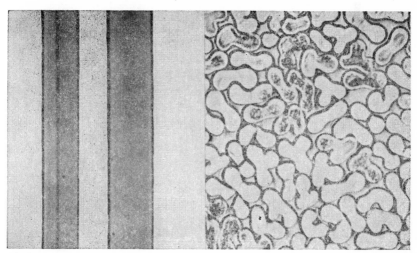

Fig. 91. Orlon® acrylic filament. (Left) Longitudinal. (Right) Cross-section.

Photomicrographs

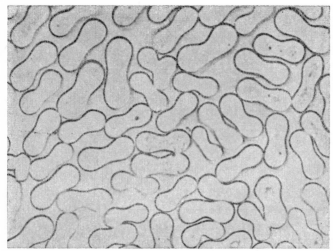

Fig. 92. Orlon® acrylic staple. Cross-section.

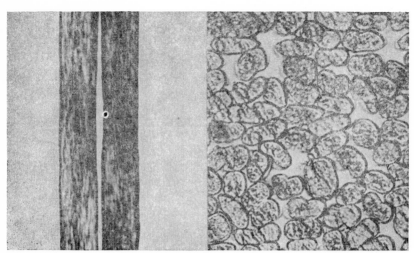

Fig. 93. Dynel® modacrylic. (Left) Longitudinal. (Right) Cross-section.

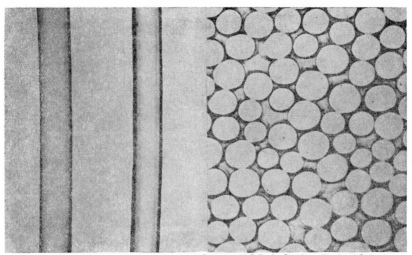

Courtesy U.S.D.A., Southern Regional Laboratory.

Fig. 94. Dacron® polyester. (Left) Longitudinal. (Right) Cross-section.

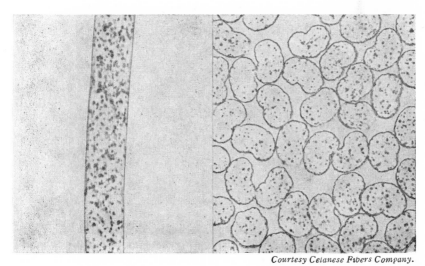

Courtesy Celanese Fibers Company.

Fig. 95. Acrilan®. (Left) Longitudinal. (Right) Cross-section.

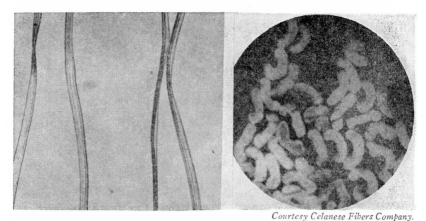

Courtesy Celanese Fibers Company.

Fig. 96. Darvan® nytril. (Left) Longitudinal. (Right) Cross-section.

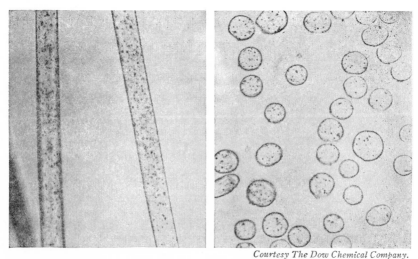

Courtesy The Dow Chemical Company.

Fig. 97. Zefran® modified acrylic. (Left) Longitudinal. (Right) Cross-section.

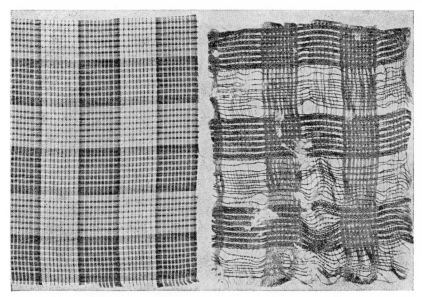

Fig. 98. Chemical test. Acetone. Combination acetate and rayon. Original (left), residue rayon (right).

clear water. Dry and mount. In case the sample is all wool or all silk, there will be no residue.

Laboratory: In laboratory practice, boil sample in a 5 per cent solution of sodium hydroxide in a beaker or evaporating dish. Wash residue in dilute acetic acid and rinse in clear water. In a blend of cotton and wool, Viyella® flannel, the residue is cotton. Fig. 100. Cotton warp, silk filling: residue, cotton. Fig. 101.

PROCEDURES FOR COMPARATIVE ANALYSIS

Standard procedure by well-trained technicians in modern laboratories to determine if fabrics meet standardized specifications. Atmospheric conditions of temperature 70° F. (±2) and relative humidity 60 per cent (±2).

Some of the important tests are:

Light fastness. Fade-Ometer®. Fig. 102.

Fig. 99. Acid test. Blend of cotton and wool. Viyella® flannel. Wool residue in center.

Fig. 100. Alkali test. Blend of cotton and wool. Viyella® flannel. Original (left), cotton residue (right).

Fig. 101. Alkali test. Cotton warp with silk filling. Original (left), residue cotton warp (right).

Tensile strength by grab or strip method. Scott tester®, Fig. 103.

Water repellency. Spray tester, Figs. 104, 105.

Percentage fiber content by chemical analysis.

Dry sample (example Viyella® flannel): Weigh on chainomatic balance; proceed with chemical test required, rinse, dry sample. Calculate percentage of residue.

Fiber analysis. See references to technique for making permanent mounts. Typical longitudinal and cross-section views of some man-made fibers. See Photomicrographs.

With calibrated instruments, additional tests can be made as: twist of yarn, abrasion, resistance, absorbency, flammability, washability, etc. See List of Instruments, Appendix.

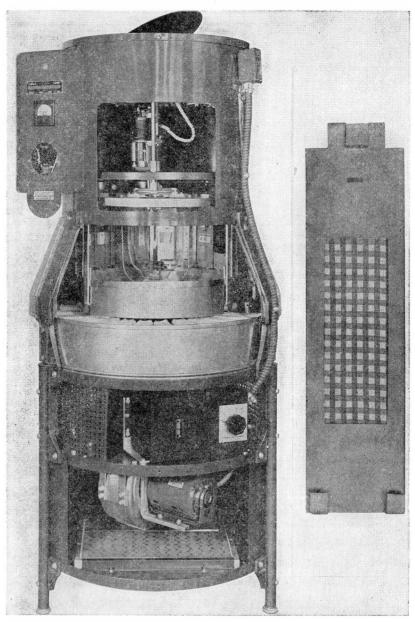

Fig. 102. Test for light fastness. Fade-Ometer®. Note sample in frame.
See Appendix, Testing equipment.

Fig. 103. Test for tensile strength. Scott tester. Model J.

Fig. 104. Test for water repellency. Spray test unit. See Appendix,
Testing equipment.

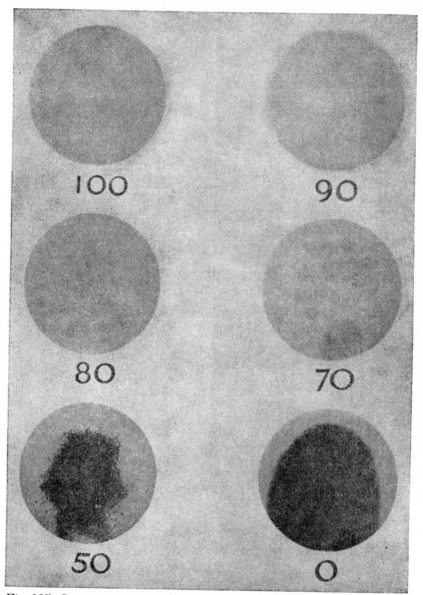

Fig. 105. Spray test rating chart. No penetration rated 100 per cent; water penetration rated 0.

Part III   Complaints on
Textile Merchandise

There are many reasons why the public does not find satisfaction in the goods it buys and uses. The following are some of the faults:

1. Shrinkage or stretch due to various causes. Example: Bath towels with woven stripes near ends. Stripe shrinks after washing; leaves ruffled effect. Fig. 106. Likewise, tablecloths with solid border stripes of different yarns or weave.

2. Slippage due to loose construction or unevenly matched warp and filling.

3. Flaw in weaving. Lumpy filling yarn piles up. Fig. 107.

4. Flock and lacquer prints not always durable to washing and dry cleaning.

5. Pilling, a fault in some woolen and synthetic fabrics due to short fibers. Friction rubs up balls on surface.

6. Bleeding or crocking may be due to fugitive dyes.

7. Tendering of curtains due to sunlight or atmospheric gases in cotton, rayon, acetate, or nylon fabrics. Fig. 108.

8. Nonpenetration of dyes; e.g. piece-dyed bengaline or fine poplin where dye does not penetrate to filling yarns.

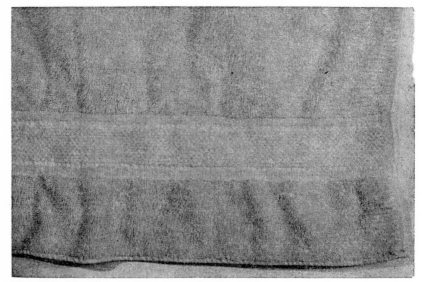

Fig. 106. Shrinkage of stripes in bath towel.

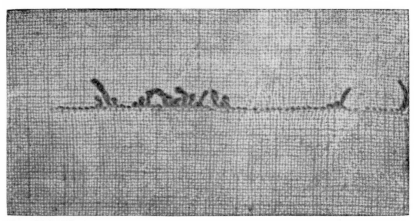

Fig. 107. Flaw in weaving.

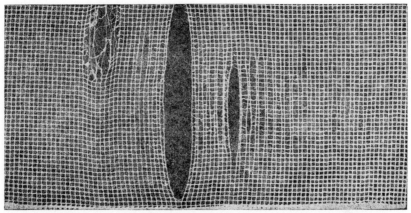

Fig. 108. Deteriorating action of sunlight on some curtain fabrics.

9. Misprint, usually found in roller printing where pattern missed in sections of the yardage, leaving blank or distorted portions.

10. Careless finishing—goods set off grain of weave in tentering frame.

Misuse of Fibers and Weaves

11. Material as nylon sheer has many uses; not adapted to glass curtains.

12. Fiberglas. Perfect for its uses but when curtains are improperly installed, abrasion may cause breaks.

13. Dress fabrics used for curtains when dye fastness is not adequate for continued exposure to sun.

Part IV   Legislation

The Federal Trade Commission was created by an Act of Congress September 26, 1914, defining its powers and duties. It is composed of five Commissioners with jurisdiction over commerce between states and with foreign nations. Its function is to investigate and prevent unfair methods of competition.

The Federal Labeling Laws:

1. Wool Products Labeling Act of 1939, became effective July 15, 1941. Its primary purpose is to protect producers, manufacturers, distributors, and consumers from the unrevealed presence of substitutes and mixtures in spun, woven, knitted, felted, or otherwise manufactured wool products.

2. Fur Products Labeling Act was passed August 8, 1951, and became effective August 9, 1952. Its purpose is to protect consumers and others against misbranding, false advertising, and false invoicing of fur products and furs.

3. Textile Fiber Products Identification Act was approved in 1958 and became effective March 3, 1960. Its primary purpose is to protect producers and consumers against misbranding and false advertising of the fiber content of textile fiber products.

Under these three acts the Federal Trade Commission conducts compliance investigations, inspections, and industry counseling. It issues registered identification numbers and records continuing guaranties. The Commission has published rules and regulations under these statutes, together with illustrations of acceptable labeling, which supply full information concerning their requirements.

The Commission has issued a register of animal names, known as the Fur Products Name Guide, for use in properly describing furs and fur products.

The Commission also administers the Flammable Fabrics Act of 1953 which became effective July 1, 1954. Its purpose is to prohibit the introduction or movement in interstate commerce of articles of wearing apparel and fabrics which are so highly flammable as to be dangerous when worn by individuals.

In addition to the cease-and-desist orders specified for FTC violations, the law also authorizes court proceedings, including criminal sanctions.

U. S. Govt. Organization Manual, 1961-62.

WOOL PRODUCTS LABELING ACT OF 1939*

Rules and Regulations
Effective July 15, 1941
Amended August 1, 1949
Amended November 14, 1953

AN ACT

To protect producers, manufacturers, distributors and consumers from the unrevealed presence of substitutes and mixtures in spun, woven, knitted, felted or otherwise manufactured wool products and for other purposes.

SECTION 2.

The term "wool" means the fiber from the fleece of the sheep or lamb or hair of the Angora or Cashmere goat (and may include the so-called specialty fibers from the hair of the camel, alpaca, llama and vicuna) which has never been reclaimed from any woven or felted wool product.

The term "reprocessed wool" means the resulting fiber when wool has been woven or felted into a wool product which, without ever having been utilized in any way by the ultimate consumer, subsequently has been made into a fibrous state.

The term "reused wool" means the resulting fiber when wool or reprocessed wool has been spun, woven, knitted, or felted into a wool product which after having been used in any way by the ultimate consumer has subsequently been made into a fibrous state.

*Brief and partial statement.

The term "wool product" means any product, or any portion of a product, which contains, purports to contain, or in any way is represented as containing, wool, reprocessed wool, or reused wool.

SECTION 3.

Introduction, or manufacture for introduction, into commerce, or the sale, transportation, or distribution, in commerce, of any wool product which is misbranded is unlawful and excludes common carriers shipping wool product in ordinary course of business and anyone exporting to foreign country a wool product branded in accordance with laws of that country. 54 Stat. 1128, 15 U.S.C.A. 68.

FUR FABRICS LABELING ACT, 1952

AN ACT

To protect consumers and others against misbranding, false advertising, and false invoicing of fur products and furs.

Amendment effective March 15, 1961.

(Federal Register Apr. 14, 1961, page 3186).

FLAMMABLE FABRICS ACT, 1953
Effective July 1, 1954
Amended to date July 1, 1958

AN ACT

To prohibit the introduction or movement in interstate commerce of articles of wearing apparel and fabrics which are so highly flammable as to be dangerous when worn by individuals and for other purposes.

(1953 U. S. Code & Administration News, 1723)

For regulation under the Act see 16 CFR Part 302.

TEXTILE FIBER PRODUCTS IDENTIFICATION ACT[*]
Approved 1958
Effective March 3, 1960

*Brief and partial statement.

Rules and regulations as amended, effective July 26, 1960
16 CFR Part 303

AN ACT

To protect producers and consumers against misbranding and false advertising of the fiber content of textile fiber products, and for other purposes.

Labels required—

Generic name and percentages of all fibers present in amounts more than 50%—listed in order of predominance by weight.

The label must disclose the name or registered number of a person or firm marketing the product in commerce as defined in Section 3 of the Act.

If such textile fiber product is imported, name of country where processed or manufactured must appear on label.

Generic names—

Name of a specific fiber family as cotton, linen, silk, wool. Manufactured fibers—16 generic groups

Acrylic	Acetate	Nylon	Olefin
Modacrylic	Saran	Rubber	Vinyon
Polyester	Azlon	Spandex	Metallic
Rayon	Nytril	Vinal	Glass

Trade marks must always be linked with generic name of the fiber to which it is related, as 65% Dacron® polyester, 35% cotton. The ® identifies the trade mark with a particular polyester fiber.

Rules and Regulations

The Federal Trade Commission has jurisdiction over the application of these rules.

Examples of labels acceptable:

Rule 6—Generic Names of Fibers to be Used:

| 80% rabbit hair | or | 80% silk |
| 20% nylon | | 20% mink fiber |

60% cotton	or	50% nylon
40% fur fiber		30% mink hair
		20% fur fiber

Rule 7—Generic Names and Definitions for Manufactured Fibers:

(a) **acrylic**—fiber-forming substance is any long chain synthetic polymer composed of at least 85% by weight of acrylonitrile units.

(b) **modacrylic**—fiber-forming substance is any long chain synthetic polymer composed of less than 85% but at least 35% by weight of acrylonitrile units.

(c) **polyester**—fiber-forming substance is any long chain synthetic polymer composed of at least 85% by weight of an ester of dihydric alcohol and terephthalic acid.

(d) **rayon**—fiber composed of regenerated cellulose.

(e) **acetate**—fiber-forming substance is cellulose acetate. Where not less than 92% of hydroxyl groups are acetylated, the term triacetate may be used as generic description of fiber.

(f) **saran**—fiber-forming substance is any long chain synthetic polymer composed of at least 80% by weight of vinylidene chloride units.

(g) **azlon**—fiber-forming substance is composed of any regenerated naturally occurring proteins.

(h) **nytril**—fiber containing at least 85% of a long chain polymer of vinylidene dinitrile.

(i) **nylon**—fiber-forming substance is any long chain synthetic polyamide having recurring amide groups as an integral part of polymer chain.

(j) **rubber**—fiber in which fiber-forming substance is comprised of natural or synthetic rubber.

(k) **spandex**—fiber-forming substance, long chain synthetic polymer comprised of at least 85% of a seg-
mented polyurethane.

(l) **vinal**—fiber-forming substance, any long chain
synthetic polymer composed of at least 50% by
weight of vinyl alcohol units and in which the
total of the vinyl alcohol units and any one or
more of the various acetal units is at least 85% by
weight of the fiber.

(m) **olefin**—fiber-forming substance, any long chain
synthetic polymer composed of at least 85% by
weight of ethylene, propylene or other olefin units.

(n) **vinyon**—fiber-forming substance is any long chain
synthetic polymer composed of at least 85% by
weight of vinyl chloride units.

(o) **metallic**—fiber composed of metal, plastic-coated
metal, metal-coated plastic, or a core completely
covered by metal.

(p) **glass**—the fiber-forming substance is glass.

TRADE PRACTICE CONFERENCE RULES

Promulgated by Federal Trade Commission

Code of Federal Regulations, CFR

Formulated with the cooperation of the industry through
voluntary conferences to prevent unfair methods of competition.

Silk industry November 4, 1938.

Revoked April 5, 1960 (25 FR 2835).

Linen industry February 1, 1941.

Revoked April 5, 1960 (25 FR 2836).

Rayon and Acetate textile industry, 1952.

Revoked April 5, 1960 (25 FR 2836).

Hosiery industry, promulgated May 15, 1941.

Amended February 7, 1942.

Revised August 30, 1960.

Terms defined: lisle cotton or cotton lisle, long-staple cotton, combed and carded yarns, crepe, irregulars, seconds,
and thirds.

AMERICAN STANDARDS[*]

American Standards Association, founded in 1918, is the clearing house for industrial, engineering, safety and consumers' standards in the United States. The ASA does not make standards; it makes standards possible. They are voluntarily adopted and approved by industries. They are not laws.

ASA L 4.1   Specifications for bleached cotton bed sheets
1948   and pillow cases

1.1 *Scope*

Combed percale. Thread count 200 or Type 200.

Combed percale. Thread count 180 or Type 180.

Carded percale. Thread count 180 or Type 180.

Heavy weight muslin. Thread count 140 or Type 140.

Medium weight muslin. Thread count 128 or Type 128.

	Type 200 Combed Yarn	Type 180 Combed or Carded Yarn	Type 140 Carded Yarn	Type 128 Carded Yarn
Combined thread count warp and filling (per inch square)	200	180	140	128
Warp breaking strength (pounds)	60	60	70	55
Filling breaking strength (pounds)	60	60	70	55
Maximum added sizing	1%	2%	4%	6%
Weight (ounces per square yard)	3.6	3.6	4.6	4.0

Note: All standards are minimum specifications with the exception of sizing which is maximum.

[*] Approved November 19, 1948 for ASA Inc. Sponsor American Hospital Association.

L22 1960*

American Standard minimum requisite for rayon and acetate fabrics. Prepared by Com. L22 est. 1949, first pub. 1953.

Fifty-one different end-uses are listed with test methods for telling whether the fabric will be suitable for the end-use specified.

Suggested color tags or sewn-in labels for fabric or garment.

Trade name—American Standard.
Red—dry cleanable
Yellow—wash at hand temp. 105° F.
Green—washable up to 160° F.

COMMERCIAL STANDARDS*

"Recorded voluntary standards of the trade"; they are not laws. Issued by the U. S. Department of Commerce Commodity Standards Division, July 1, 1959.

Purpose, to establish standard quality requirements, methods of test ratings, certification and procedure for uniform bases for fair competition. Developed by voluntary cooperation among manufacturers, distributors and consumers. The following is an example:

Commercial Standard CS 191-53—
Flammability of Clothing Textiles
Effective date January 30, 1953.

FEDERAL SPECIFICATIONS*

Revised March, 1962

They are not laws, but tools for government purchasing: Army, Navy, Air Force; military agencies, as veterans' hospitals. The following are a few examples:

L 4.1—1948	Textile Testing Methods.
CCC—T—191a	amended May 15, 1951 and January 15, 1959.

	Sheets, Cotton, bleached.
CCC—T—191b	December 28, 1959.
DDD—S—281e	

	Cloth, cotton, sheeting.
CCC—C—430a	December 18, 1961

*Brief and partial statement.

References

Bergen, Werner von, and Krauss, Walter. *Textile Fiber Atlas.* Textile Book Publishers, Inc., 1942, rev. 1952. 303 Fifth Avenue, New York 16, N. Y.

Bergen, von, and Mauersberger, H. R. *American Wool Handbook.* Textile Book Publishers, Inc., New York. 2nd ed., 1948.

Fairchild's Dictionary of Textiles. Ed., Stephen S. Marks, Fairchild Publications, Inc., New York, 1959.

Haven, G. B. *Handbook of Industrial Fabrics.* Textile Book Publishers, Inc., New York, 1954.

Hess, Katharine P. *Textile Fibers and Their Use.* 6th ed., J. B. Lippincott Co., Philadelphia, Pa., 1958.

Hollen, Mary, and Saddler, Jane. *Textiles.* The Macmillan Co., New York, 1955.

Linton, George E. *Applied Textiles,* 6th ed., and *The Modern Textile Dictionary—1962-63.* Both published by Duell, Sloan & Pearce, Div. Meredith Press, Inc., Des Moines, Ia.

Mauersberger, H. R. *Matthew's Textile Fibers.* 6th ed., John Wiley & Sons, Inc., New York, 1954.

Moncrieff, R. W. *Man-made Fibers.* 3rd ed., John Wiley & Sons, Inc., New York, 1957.

Potter, M. David, and Corbman, Bernard P. *Fiber and Fabrics.* 3rd ed., McGraw-Hill Book Co., Inc., New York, 1959.

Stout, Evelyn E. *Introduction to Textiles.* John Wiley & Sons, Inc., New York, 1960.

Textile Handbook published by American Home Economics Association, 1960.

BOOKLETS, BULLETINS, PAMPHLETS, AND PERIODICALS

American Association of Textile Chemists & Colorists (AATCC)
1959 Technical Manual. P. O. Box 28, Lowell, Mass.

American Dyestuffs Reporter. Monthly (to members of AATCC),
44 E. 23rd St., New York, N. Y.

American Fabrics. Monthly, 24 E. 38th St., New York 16, N. Y.

American Society for Testing Materials. (ASTM) 1916 Race St.,
Philadelphia, Pa.
Standards on Textile Materials, Committee D-13, 1961.

American Standards Association, 10 E. 40th St., New York 16,
N. Y. ASA L22 Vol. I, approved Feb. 11, 1960. Vol. II,
Test methods to be used with L22 standards.

Identification of Fibers in Textile Materials, Multi-Fiber Bulletin
X-156, E. I. du Pont de Nemours, *et al.,* Textile Fibers Dept.,
Wilmington, Delaware, 1961.

Man-made Fabrics and Yarns. Pub. by Textile World, Man-
made Fiber Table 1960 Supplement, 330 W. 42nd Street, New
York 36.

Modern Textiles Magazine, formerly *Rayon & Synthetic Textiles
and Rayon Textile Monthly,* 303 Fifth Avenue, New York 16.

Textile World. Monthly, 330 West 42nd St., New York 36.

USDA Leaflet No. 454—*Making Household Fabrics Flame Resistant.* 1959.

Appendix

Abraser:
 Tabor Instrument Corp.,
 111 Goundry St., No. Tonawanda, N. Y.
Chainomatic balance:
 Christian Becker, New York City.
Conditioning (radiant heat) oven: Cat. #3500
 Labline Inc.
Fade-Ometer®: Fig. 102.
 Atlas Electric Devices Co.,
 4114 No. Ravenswood Ave., Chicago 13, Ill.
Flammability tester: brushing device:
 U. S. Testing Co.,
 1415 Park Ave., Hoboken, N. J.
Gas fading test chamber:
 U. S. Testing Co.
Launder-Ometer®:
 Atlas Electric Devices Co.
Linen tester ×5 Fig. 78.
 Bausch & Lomb Optical Co.,
 Rochester 2, N. Y.
Microscopes:
 Student microscope No. AO66B Fig. 82.
 Cycloptic No. 56F-1 Fig. 83.
 American Optical Co., Instrument Div.,
 Buffalo 15, N. Y.

Scott Tester® Model J   Fig. 103.
    Scott Testers Inc.
    101 Blackstone St., P. O. Box 963, Providence, R. I.
Spray test unit   Fig. 104.
Spray test rating chart   Fig. 105.
    American Association of Textile Chemists & Colorists
    Box 28, Lowell, Mass.

REGISTERED TRADE NAMES*

Acele® acetate.	E. I. du Pont de Nemours & Company 350 Fifth Ave., New York
Acrilan®.	Chemstrand Corporation 350 Fifth Ave., New York
Agilon®.	Deering Milliken Research Corp. 1045 Sixth Ave., New York
Antron® nylon.	E. I. du Pont de Nemours & Company
Armo®.	Arms Textile Mfg. Co. Div. of Crown Textile Mfg. Co. 1407 Broadway, New York
Arnel® triacetate.	Celanese Fibers Co. 522 Fifth Ave., New York
Asbeston®.	United States Rubber Company 1230 Sixth Ave., New York
Avicron®.	American Viscose Corporation 1617 Pennsylvania Blvd. Philadelphia, Pa.
Avisco® acetate.	American Viscose Corporation
Avisco® rayon.	American Viscose Corporation
Avlin®.	American Viscose Corporation
Avril®.	American Viscose Corporation
Avron® viscose.	American Viscose Corporation

* ® in every definition indicates registered trade mark.

BanCare®.	Joseph Bancroft & Sons Co.
	Wilmington, Del.
Ban-Flame®.	Joseph Bancroft & Sons Co.
Ban-Lon®.	Joseph Bancroft & Sons Co.
	Everglaze Marketing Div.
Belfast®.	Deering Milliken Research Corp.
Bemberg	Beaunit Mills, Inc.
	261 Fifth Ave., New York
Bondex®.	Permacel Corporation
	New Brunswick, N. J.
Bontex®.	Columbus Coated Fabrics Corp.
	Columbus, Ohio
Byrd cloth®.	Reeves Bros. Inc.
	1071 Sixth Ave., New York
Cadon® nylon.	Chemstrand Corporation
Caprolan®.	Chemstrand Corporation
Celanese® acetate.	Celanese Fibers Co.
Celanese® celaspun.	Celanese Fibers Co.
Celaperm® acetate.	Celanese Fibers Co.
Charmeen®.	J. P. Stevens & Co.
	Forstmann Division
	1460 Broadway, New York
Chemstrand® nylon.	Chemstrand Corporation
Chromefast®.	Sears Roebuck & Company
	Chicago, Illinois
Chromspun®.	Eastman Chemical Products Inc.
	260 Madison Ave., New York
Coloray® viscose.	Courtauld's (Alabama)
	600 Fifth Ave., New York
Colorspun®.	American Viscose Corporation
Combat cloth®.	J. P. Stevens & Co.
	William Skinner & Sons
	12 West 40th St., New York
Contro®.	Firestone Tire & Rubber Co.
	45 Rockefeller Plaza, New York

Cordino®.	J. C. Penney Co.
	330 W. 34th St., New York
Corduro® viscose.	E. I. du Pont de Nemours & Company
Corval®.	Courtauld's (Alabama)
Cotron®.	American Viscose Corporation
Cravenette®.	The Cravenette Co., U.S.A.
	60 Romanelli Ave.
	So. Hackensack, N. J.
Creslan® acrylic.	American Cyanamid Co.
	111 W. 40th St., New York
Cupioni®.	Beaunit Mills, Inc.
Cuprammonium®.	American Bemberg Div.
	Beaunit Mills, Inc.
Curad®.	Bauer & Black
	Division Kendall Co.
	309 W. Jackson Blvd.
	Chicago, Illinois
Curon®.	Reeves Bros. Inc.
Cyana®.	American Cyanamid Co.
Dacron® fiber-fill.	E. I. du Pont de Nemours & Company
Dacron® polyester.	E. I. du Pont de Nemours & Company
Day-glo®.	Switzer Brothers, Inc.
	Cleveland, Ohio
Disciplined®.	Bates Manufacturing Company
	112 W. 34th St., New York
Dri-don®.	Dan River Mills
	111 W. 40th St., New York
du Pont nylon®.	E. I. du Pont de Nemours & Company
du Pont rayon®.	E. I. du Pont de Nemours & Company
Durene®.	Dixie Mercerizing Co.
	Chattanooga, Tenn.
Dylanize®.	Dylanize Laboratories
	No. Providence, R. I.

	Stevenson's, Inc.
	21 E. 40th St., New York
Dynel® modacrylic.	Union Carbide Corporation
	100 E. 42nd St., New York
Enka® rayon.	American Enka Corporation
	350 Fifth Ave., New York
Enka® nylon.	American Enka Corporation
Estron® acetate.	Eastman Chemical Products Inc.
Everfast®.	Everfast Fabrics, Inc.
	70 W. 40th St., New York
Everglaze®.	Joseph Bancroft & Sons Co.
	Everglaze Marketing Div.
Evershrunk®.	Everfast Fabrics, Inc.
Fabrikoid®.	E. I. du Pont de Nemours & Company
Fabrilite®.	E. I. du Pont de Nemours & Company
Feutron®.	American Felt Company
	Glenville, Conn.
Fiberglas®.	Owens-Corning Fiberglas Corp.
	717 Fifth Ave., New York
Fiberset®.	Bianchini, Ferier Inc.
	663 Fifth Ave., New York
Formite®.	David B. Carmel & Co.
	1407 Broadway, New York
Fortisan® rayon.	Celanese Fibers Co.
Fortrel® polyester.	Celanese Fibers Co.
	Fiber Industries, Inc.
Gerona®.	J. P. Stevens & Co.
	Forstmann Division
Glosheen®.	Waverly Fabrics
	Div. of F. Schumacher Co.
	60 W. 40th St., New York

Harris tweed®.	Harris Tweed Assoc. Ltd.
	London, England
	Harris Tweed Assn.
	295 Madison Ave., New York
Heberlein®.	Heberlein Patent Corporation
	350 Fifth Ave., New York
Helanca®.	Heberlein Patent Corporation
Indian head®.	Indian Head Mills
	111 W. 40th St., New York
Interlon®.	Stacy Fabrics Corporation
	469 Seventh Ave., New York
Jetspun®.	American Enka Corporation
Kenisan®.	Sears Roebuck & Company
Keybak®.	Chicopee Mills
	47 Worth St., New York
Kodel® polyester.	Eastman Chemical Products, Inc.
Koroseal®.	B. F. Goodrich Company
	Plastic Products Div.
	Cleveland, Ohio
Kroy®.	York Knitting Process Co.
	70 Crawford St.
	Toronto, Ontario
Lacelon®.	Minnesota Mining
	and Manufacturing Company
	900 Bush Ave.,
	St. Paul, Minnesota
Lame®.	Standard Yarn Mills Inc.
	6205 30th Ave.,
	Woodside, L. I., New York
Lanaset®.	American Cyanamid Co.
Lanella®.	Lanella Corporation
	185 Madison Ave., New York
Lastex®.	U. S. Rubber Co., Lastex Yarn Division
	1230 Sixth Ave., New York

Liberty®.	Liberty of London
	London, England
Lorganza®.	Bianchini, Ferier Inc.
Lumarith®.	Celanese Fibers Co.
Lumite®.	Chicopee Mills, Lumite Div.
	47 Worth St., New York
Lurex®.	The Dow Chemical Company
	Williamsburg, Va.
Lycra® spandex.	E. I. du Pont de Nemours & Company
Macintosh®.	Robert Appleby & Co., selling agent
	250 Park Ave., New York
Martinized®.	Martin Fabrics Corporation
	48 W. 38th St., New York
Marvella®.	J. P. Stevens & Co.
	Forstmann Division
Masslinn®.	Chicopee Mills
Meraklon®.	Chemore Corporation
	100 E. 42nd St., New York
	Celanese Fibers Co.
Metlon®.	Metlon Corporation
	Div. Reynolds Metals Co.
	432 Fourth Ave., New York
Milium®.	Deering Milliken Co., Milium Division
	1045 Sixth Ave., New York
Mitin®.	Geigy Dyestuffs
	89 Barclay St., New York
Moygashel®.	Hamilton Adams Imports, Ltd.
	24 W. 40th St., New York
Moynel® polynosic.	Courtaulds, Alabama
Mylar®.	E. I. du Pont de Nemours & Company
Narco® viscose.	Beaunit Mills, Inc.
Naugahyde®.	U. S. Rubber Company
Norane®.	Warwick Chemical Co.
	Division, Sun Chemical Corporation
	Wood River Junction, Rhode Island

Nymo®.	Belding Corticelli Co.
	1407 Broadway, New York
Orlon® acrylic.	E. I. du Pont de Nemours & Company
Orlon cantrece®.	E. I. du Pont de Nemours & Company
Palm beach®.	Palm Beach Co.
	200 Fifth Ave., New York
Pellon®.	Pellon Corporation
	Empire State Bldg., New York
Pelomite®.	Pellon Corporation
Permacel®.	Permacel Corporation
Permel Plus®.	American Cyanamid Company
Pliofilm®.	Goodyear Tire & Rubber Co.
	Akron, Ohio
Polo cloth®.	Worumbo Div., J. P. Stevens & Co.
Powder puff®.	Dumari Textiles Co. Inc.
	70 W. 40th St., New York
Pyroset®.	American Cyanamid Co.
Ramona® cloth.	J. C. Penney
Reevon® olefin.	Reeves Brothers, Inc.
Resloom®.	Monsanto Chemical Co., Plastics Div.
	Springfield, Mass.
Reymet®.	Reynolds Metals Co.
	19 E. 47th St., New York
Rhovyl®.	Rhodia Inc.
	60 E. 56th St., New York
Rigmel®.	Bradford Dyeing Association
	111 W. 40th St., New York
Ripplette®.	Bates Manufacturing Company
	112 W. 34th St., New York
Rovana® saran.	The Dow Chemical Co.
	Textile Fabrics. Dept.
	350 Fifth Ave., New York

Sanforized®.	Sanforized (Div. of Cluett, Peabody)
	530 Fifth Ave., New York
Sanforized plus®.	Sanforized
Sanitized®.	Sanitized, Inc.
	369 Lexington Ave., New York
Saranspun® saran.	J. P. Stevens & Co.
	Plastic Products Division
	Odenton, Maryland
Sasheen®.	Minnesota Mining
	and Manufacturing Company
Scotch®.	Minnesota Mining
	and Manufacturing Company
Scotch dusting fabric®.	Minnesota Mining
	and Manufacturing Company
Scotchgard®.	Minnesota Mining
	and Manufacturing Company
Scotchlite®.	Minnesota Mining
	and Manufacturing Company
Scott Apparel Foam®.	Scott Paper Co., Foam Division
	350 Fifth Ave., New York
Shagbark®.	Burlington Industries, Inc.
	Galey & Lord Division
	1407 Broadway, New York
Simtex®.	J. P. Stevens & Co.
Spun-lo®.	Industrial Rayon Corporation
	Union Commerce Bldg.
	Cleveland, Ohio
Stazenu®.	Joseph Bancroft & Sons Co.
Sunbak®.	J. P. Stevens & Co.
	William Skinner & Sons
Sundour®.	J. H. Thorp & Co., Inc.
	425 E. 53rd St., New York
Super Siri®.	David B. Carmel & Co.
SuPima®.	SuPima Association of America
	112 W. 34th St., New York

Suracel®.	Avondale Mills Inc.
	1430 Broadway, New York
Syl-Mer®.	Dow Corning Corp.
	717 Fifth Ave., New York
Tackle twill®.	J. P. Stevens & Co.
	William Skinner & Sons Co.
Talon Zephyr®.	Talon, Inc.
	Meadville, Pennsylvania
Tarpoon®.	Burlington Industries, Inc.
	Galey & Lord Division
Taslan®.	Bransom & Company (du Pont)
	1808 Liberty Life Bldg.
	Charlotte, N. C.
Tebilized®.	T. B. Lee Company, Inc.
	1441 Broadway, New York
	Tootal Broadhurst Lee
	Company, Ltd.
	Manchester, England
Tempra® viscose.	American Enka Corporation
Terylene®.	Imperial Chemical Industries, Ltd.
	London, England
	488 Madison Ave., New York
Texcel®.	Permacel Corporation
Textralized®.	Joseph Bancroft & Sons
Tontine®.	E. I. du Pont de Nemours & Company
Topel®.	Courtauld's (Alabama)
Trilok®.	U. S. Rubber Co.
Tycora®.	Textured Yarn Co. Inc.
	40 E. 34th St., New York
Tyrex®.	Beaunit Mills, Inc.
	350 Fifth Ave., New York
Tyron® viscose.	American Viscose Corp.
Velcro®.	American Velcro, Inc.
	Dow and Canal Streets, Manchester, N. H.

Velon® saran.	Velon Plastics Division
	Firestone Tire and Rubber Co.
Verel® modacrylic.	Eastman Chemical Products Co.
Visca®.	American Viscose Corporation
Viyella®.	William Hollins & Co., Inc.
	347 Madison Ave., New York
Vycron® polyester.	Beaunit Mills, Inc.
Vyrene® spandex.	U. S. Rubber Co.,Textile Division
	Rockefeller Center, New York
Wrinkl-shed®.	Dan River Mills
Zantrel® polynosic.	Hartford Fibers Co.
	Bigelow Sanford Carpet Co.
	140 Madison Ave., New York
Zefran® acrylic.	The Dow Chemical Co.
Zelan®.	E. I. du Pont de Nemours & Company
Zeset®.	E. I. du Pont de Nemours & Company